TEMPERATURE
REGULATION

THE WYKEHAM SCIENCE SERIES

General Editors:
PROFESSOR SIR NEVILL MOTT, F.R.S.
Emeritus Cavendish Professor of Physics
University of Cambridge

G. R. NOAKES
Formerly Senior Physics Master
Uppingham School

Biological Editor:
W. B. YAPP
Formerly Senior Lecturer
University of Birmingham

The aim of the Wykeham Science Series is to introduce the present state of the many fields of study within science to students approaching or starting their careers in University, Polytechnic, or College of Technology. Each book seeks to reinforce the link between school and higher education, and the main author, a distinguished worker or teacher in the field, is assisted by an experienced sixth form schoolmaster.

TEMPERATURE REGULATION

S. A. Richards – Wye College
(University of London)

WYKEHAM PUBLICATIONS (LONDON) LTD
(A MEMBER OF THE TAYLOR & FRANCIS GROUP)
LONDON AND WINCHESTER
1973

First published 1973 by Wykeham Publications (London) Ltd.

Cover illustration—King penguins

ISBN 0 85109 360 4   (paper)
ISBN 0 85109 390 6   (cloth)

Printed in Great Britain by Taylor & Francis Ltd.
10–14 Macklin Street, London, WC2B 5NF

Distribution:

UNITED KINGDOM, EUROPE, MIDDLE EAST AND AFRICA

Chapman & Hall Ltd. (a member of Associated Book Publishers Ltd.), 11 New Fetter Lane, London, EC4P 4EE, and North Way Andover Hampshire.

WESTERN HEMISPHERE

Springer-Verlag New York Inc., 175 Fifth Avenue, New York, New York 10010.

AUSTRALIA AND NEW GUINEA

Hicks Smith & Sons Pty. Ltd., 301 Kent Street, Sydney, N.S.W. 2000.

NEW ZEALAND AND FIJI

Hicks Smith & Sons Ltd., 238 Wakefield Street, Wellington.

ALL OTHER TERRITORIES

Taylor & Francis Ltd., 10–14 Macklin Street, London, WC2B 5NF.

PREFACE

MANY aspects of physiology are best understood in terms of bodily reactions to environmental stress, and temperature is one of the most often encountered stress factors in the environment. The responses to temperature can involve practically all of the organ systems of the body and it is for this reason that the study of the regulation of body temperatures represents one of the finest examples of complex reaction integrated by the nervous and endocrine systems, and hence of the principles of biological control. Thus, while thermoregulation offers an abundance of opportunities for the individual who likes to specialize in depth, it is an ideal type of physiology for those who prefer to think of the functioning of the body as whole.

This book is written primarily for the undergraduate, but I hope also that some students may find time to read it, before embarking on a university course, as an introduction to some of the ideas that will be encountered in the more detailed study of the biological sciences, including medicine. I have tried to discuss the evidence for important ideas, since this is fundamental to the scientific method, and have been particularly concerned to avoid the use of the sort of technical jargon that gives a spurious impression of authority while in reality creating confusion out of what is in essence simple.

Since the book is intended to provide only a framework for further study, the reading list is restricted largely to monographs and review articles. These in turn refer to the original research papers. Many of the species discussed in the text may be unfamiliar to the reader and, accordingly, they have all been gathered together in a classification at the end of the book.

The ' Système International d'Unités ' (SI) is used throughout. While the new system presents something of a traumatic challenge to virtually all practising biologists, an introductory book must follow a clear lead rather than perpetuate differences. Our old departed friends, most notably perhaps the calorie, will be no more than clumsy accidents of history to the new generation of scientists. The units are defined in the preliminary tables, and factors are provided for their conversion to and from the traditional units. The main authority has been the Royal Society's 'Quantities, Units, and Sybmols' (1971; its rules have as closly as possibly, been followed.

I am grateful to the authors and publishers who have allowed me to make use of their own material and trust that they will be lenient with me if they do not wholly approve of the ways in which I have modified and redrawn their illustrations to suit my own purpose or to conform to the SI regulations. I should also like to thank Mr. P. S. Fielden, who undertook to read and criticise the text and figures with his experienced teacher's eye, and particularly Mr. W. B. Yapp, who kindly invited me to write the book in the first instance and who gave me the benefit of his immense breadth of biological knowledge in the shape of a host of constructive comments.

CONTENTS

Preface   v

Principal Subscripts used in the text   viii

Special Quantities of use in Thermal Physiology   ix

Conversion Factors   x

Quantities and Symbols   xi

Chapter 1   INTRODUCTION   1

Chapter 2   PHYSICAL HEAT EXCHANGE   22

Chapter 3   PHYSIOLOGICAL REGULATION OF
             HEAT PRODUCTION   40

Chapter 4   PHYSIOLOGICAL REGULATION OF
             HEAT LOSS   72

Chapter 5   BEHAVIOURAL THERMOREGULATION   110

Chapter 6   MECHANISMS CONTROLLING BODY
             TEMPERATURE   143

Chapter 7   ANIMALS AND CLIMATE   178

Bibliography   198

Glossary   199

Appendix   201

Index   206

PRINCIPAL SUBSCRIPTS USED IN THE TEXT

Significance	*Symbol*		*Example*
air	a	I_a	insulation of the air
arterial	ar	T_{ar}	temperature of arterial blood
body	b	T_b	body temperature
brain	br	T_{br}	brain temperature
core	c	T_c	core body temperature
clothing	cl	I_{cl}	insulation of clothing
colonic	co	T_{co}	colonic temperature
environmental	en	T_{en}	environmental temperature
		P_{en}	vapour pressure of environment
external	ex	I_{ex}	external insulation (from skin to environment)
hypothalamic	hy	T_{hy}	hypothalamic temperature
internal	in	I_{in}	internal insulation (from core to skin)
muscle	mu	T_{mu}	muscle temperature
rectal	r	T_r	rectal temperature
respiratory tract	re	E_{re}	evaporation from respiratory tract
		P_{re}	vapour pressure of respiratory tract
set-point	set	T_{set}	set-point temperature
skin	sk	Q_{sk}	blood flow to skin
		T_{sk}	skin temperature
surface	su	T_{su}	temperature of surface
tympanic membrane	ty	T_{ty}	temperature of tympanic membrane
venous	ve	T_{ve}	temperature of venous blood
water	wa	T_{wa}	water temperature

SPECIAL QUANTITIES OF USE IN THERMAL PHYSIOLOGY

Quantity	Symbol	Unit
convective heat exchange (+for net loss)	C	W m^{-2}
temperature difference	ΔT	K
evaporative heat loss	E	W m^{-2}
rate of loss of heat	H_L	W m^{-2}
conductive heat exchange (+for net loss)	K	W m^{-2}
rate of metabolic heat production	M	W m^{-2}
radiant heat exchange (+for net loss)	R	W m^{-2}
relative humidity	rh	per cent
heat storage (+for net heat gain by body)	S	W m^{-2}
rate of loss of temperature (cooling)	T_L	K s^{-1}
area of wetness	A_W	m^2

CONVERSION FACTORS

To convert from: (name of old unit and symbol)	To: (name of SI unit and symbol)	Multiply by
calorie (cal)	joule (J)	4·1855
kilocalorie (kcal)	joule (J)	4186·0
	kilojoule (kJ)	4·1855
calorie per second (cal s^{-1})	watt (W)	4·1855
kilocalorie per hour (kcal h^{-1})	watt (W)	1·163
kilopond metre per minute (kpm min^{-1})	watt (W)	0·1634
kilocalorie per square metre per hour $(\text{kcal m}^{-2} \text{ h}^{-1})$	watt per square metre (W m^{-2})	1·163
kilocalorie per square metre hour and degree centigrade $(\text{kcal m}^{-2} \text{ h}^{-1} \text{ }^\circ\text{C}^{-1})$	watt per square metre and kelvin $(\text{W m}^{-2} \text{ K}^{-1})$	1·163
degree centigrade, square metre and hour per kilocalorie $(^\circ\text{C m}^{-2} \text{ h kcal}^{-1})$	kelvin and square metre per watt $(\text{K m}^2 \text{ W}^{-1})$	1·163
millimetre of mercury (mm Hg)	pascal (Pa) or newton per square metre (N m^{-2})	133·3
feet per second (ft s^{-1})	metre per second (m s^{-1})	0·3048
miles per hour (mph)	metre per second (m s^{-1})	0·447

QUANTITIES AND SYMBOLS

Quantity and symbol	SI unit and symbol
amount of a substance (n)	mole (mol); millimole (mmol)
area (A)	square metre (m^2)
conductivity, thermal (k)	watt per metre per kelvin $(W\ m^{-1}\ K^{-1})$
emissivity (radiation) (ϵ)	watt per square metre $(W\ m^{-2})$
frequency (f)	hertz $(Hz) = s^{-1}$
heat, rate of exchange (H)	watt per square metre $(W\ m^{-2})$
heat, specific latent (l)	joule per kilogram $(J\ kg^{-1})$
heat, quantity (energy) (Q)	joule (J); kilojoule (kJ)
heat transfer coefficient (h)	watt per square metre per kelvin $(W\ m^{-2}\ K^{-1})$
length (l); thickness (d)	metre (m); millimetre (mm); kilometre (km)
mass (m)	gram (g); kilogram (kg)
pressure (p)	pascal (Pa) or newton per square metre $(N\ m^{-2})$; kilopascal (kPa)
resistance, thermal (insulation) (I)	kelvin and square metre per watt $(k\ m^2\ W^{-1})$
specific heat capacity (c)	joule per kilogram per kelvin $(J\ kg^{-1}\ K^{-1})$
temperature (T)*	degree Celsius (°C); kelvin (K)
temperature interval	kelvin (K)
time (t)	second (s); minute (min); hour (h); day (d)
velocity, linear (v)	metre per second $(m\ s^{-1})$
ventilation rate $(\dot{V})$†	cubic metre per second $(m^3\ s^{-1})$; litre per second $(l\ s^{-1})$
volume (V)‡	cubic metre (m^3); litre (1 or dm^3); millilitre (ml or cm^3)
work rate (power) (W)	watt $(W) = J\ s^{-1}$

* Capital (or upper case T is used here, as in scientific work generally as the symbol for temperature, whether expressed in degrees Celsius or in kelvins. Confusion between the two is unlikely, as customary temperatures are read in °C. (The Royal Society of Medicine recommends t). As a temperature interval, a *difference* of one kelvin is exactly the same as a *difference* of one degree C. In, this book K always represents a temperature interval.

† A dot over any symbol denotes the time rate of change.

‡ The litre (l) is a unit approved for use in conjunction with the SI.

CHAPTER 1

introduction

1.1. *TEMPERATURE AND LIFE*

ANIMALS are inseparable from their environments. They live in a state of close interaction between the complex physical and chemical processes of their own bodies and the variable conditions which surround them ; continuous exchanges of energy occur not only within the organism and the environment, but also between them. The energy necessary for the life process itself is generated ultimately from the oxidation of carbon and hydrogen, a reaction which yields heat, and it is for this reason that the rate at which heat is produced by an organism is used to assess the intensity of the chemical reactions, or metabolism, going on within it. Because oxidation liberates heat the temperature of any metabolizing body tends to be somewhat above that of its surroundings, although its actual temperature at a given moment represents a balance between the rate at which it produces heat by metabolism and the rate at which heat is lost by physical transfer to the environment. Such heat transfer is subject to wide fluctuations, and since temperature has a profound influence on the velocity of all chemical and physical reactions, the environment typically exerts a control over metabolic rate which is greater than any available to the animal itself.

1.1.1. *Range of Temperatures Compatible with Life*

Natural air temperatures on earth range from as low as $-65°C$ in the Antarctic to as high as $60°C$ in the low-latitude deserts. The normal open aquatic environment is less variable, temperatures ranging from $-2°C$ to about $40°C$; in the open ocean the range is under $30°C$, so that in thermal extremes, as in many other ways, water is a less hazardous medium than the dry land. The fact that a few bacteria and certain species of algae live in hot springs at temperatures of up to $89°C$ should serve to remind us of the extraordinary adaptability of life under exceptional conditions.

The fundamental problem facing the organism, whether on land or in water, is to maintain its body in a condition which permits the normal activity of its chemical systems. The maximum temperature range over which the cellular processes essential to life are viable is not more than 50 K. The lower limit of this is about 2 K below the freezing point of pure water, and arctic fishes well adapted to extreme cold manage to tolerate such conditions by increasing the osmoconcentration of

1

solutes in their body fluids, thereby depressing their freezing point to below the temperature of the surrounding sea water ; in effect they add an antifreeze to their blood. With most creatures, however, cold-death occurs well above the point at which actual freezing of the tissues begins, presumably because the rate of energy production falls below the minimum level necessary for basic maintenance.

The upper temperature limit of life is generally thought to be that at which denaturation of proteins (including enzymes) occurs, a process which causes irreparable damage both to their molecular structure and to their metabolic properties. The liquefaction of fats may also be involved, but in any case over-heating often leads to death before such changes occur, commonly from desiccation. The optimum body temperature in many animals is a good deal closer to the point of heat-death than to that of cold-death, as is seen most strikingly in birds since they maintain a temperature only 4–5 K below the point at which enzyme inactivation begins. By contrast, many of the warm-blooded birds and mammals can be cooled by as much as 20 K below their normal body temperature and then, if re-warmed carefully, will recover completely.

1.1.2. *Rates of Biological Activities : the van't Hoff Effect*

The velocity of a typical chemical reaction is accelerated by a rise in temperature. The quantitative relationship between the temperature and the reaction rate was first expressed by the Dutch physicist Jacobus van't Hoff (1852–1911) in the form of a simple equation :

$$Q_{10} = \frac{Rate_{(T+10)}}{Rate_{(T)}}$$

where the expression Q_{10}, now widely known as the van't Hoff or temperature coefficient, is the increase in the velocity of the reaction for a 10 K rise in temperature. The Q_{10} value for chemical reactions usually lies between 2 and 3, and is approximately constant over a wide range of temperature, so that the curve of reaction rate will be exponential (fig. 1.1).

More generally the temperature coefficient equation may be written :

$$Q_{10} = \left(\frac{K_1}{K_2}\right)^{10/(T_1 - T_2)}$$

in which K_1 and K_2 are the velocity constants at the two temperatures. If we use the logarithmic form :

$$\log Q_{10} = 10 \frac{(\log K_1 - \log K_2)}{(T_1 - T_2)}$$

it will be simple to calculate the coefficient even when measurements are available only for intervals other than 10 K.

2

For many biological processes, for example enzymatic reactions, the Q_{10} is also between 2 and 3, although the precise value may change over the tolerable temperature range. However, it is well to remember that Q_{10} values for the thermal inactivation of enzymes, and hence of heat-death, are of the order of several hundreds.

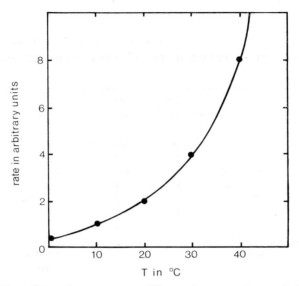

Fig. 1.1. The effect of temperature (T) on the rate of a typical biological reaction. With a Q_{10} of 2, the rate doubles for each 10 K rise in temperature. (The use of arbitrary units is permissible when a general quantitative relationship is described between two parameters, the specific dimensions of one or both of which may not be defined.)

1.2. *POIKILOTHERMY AND HOMOIOTHERMY*

1.2.1. *Metabolism and Body Temperature*

As we have seen, the temperature of an animal's body is largely dependent upon the intensity of its metabolic activity, and the rate of this activity is, in turn, determined in most animals by the temperature of the environment. Body temperature therefore tends to follow more or less passively that of the surroundings, as dictated by the laws of thermodynamics (fig. 1.2), and because the surroundings tend to be cooler than man's body temperature most animals feel cold when we touch them. The term cold-blooded, as it is applied to these creatures, appears to derive from this subjective sensation. It says no more than that the skin of the observer's fingers is warmer than that part of the surface of the animal that he touched. When we begin to consider the

3

immense complexity of the subject of temperature regulation we shall soon see that the sensation has little significance and the term itself little scientific merit.

The adjective poikilothermic, which has been used for many years as a synonym for cold-blooded, is in fact a considerable improvement since it indicates not that the animal's body temperature is ' cold ', but that it is variable (*poikilos*, many-coloured and hence changeful). The variability occurs because the rate at which the poikilotherm can produce heat by metabolism is insignificant compared to the rate at which heat is exchanged with the environment. This is why all creatures, with the

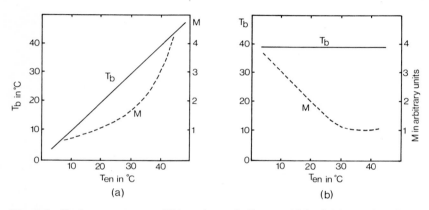

Fig. 1.2. Body temperature (T_b) and metabolic rate (M) of (*a*) a poikilotherm and (*b*) a homoiotherm in relation to environmental temperature (T_{en}).

exception of most of the birds and mammals, are soon rendered quiescent by a drop in temperature, even though they may be highly active on a warm day or even in cool air provided there is plenty of direct sun.

In modern physiology, however, the term poikilothermic is going out of favour because we see that it was coined at a time when ' animal heat ' was thought to be a simple and clear-cut subject. That is, it is a static term which conveys no information about dynamic function. The mechanisms by which an animal achieves its thermal state are better appreciated if we employ a term which reminds us that body temperature reflects the balance between the two processes of heat gain and heat loss. When the rate of heat production by metabolism is low in relation to the rate of heat loss to the surroundings, body temperature is independent of metabolic rate and determined solely by the temperature of the environment. The great majority of animals are of this type and they are now often described as ectothermic (*ektos*, outside).

The mammals and birds are exceptional in that they maintain body temperatures which are relatively constant and therefore independent of natural variations in environmental temperature. They are known popularly as ' warm-blooded ' animals, and the relative constancy of their body temperature is indicated by the term homoiothermic (*homoio-*, similar). These creatures have achieved freedom from the effects of the physical laws of heat flow because they are capable of generating large and variable quantities of heat by means of their own oxidative metabolism (fig. 1.2). Since they produce their own heat internally, these animals are called endothermic (*endon*, within).

It is important to realize that the distinction between endothermic and ectothermic animals, like most distinctions in biology, is not rigid or wholly clear-cut. Although it is true that examples of continuously endothermic animals are to be found only among the mammals and birds, some species from these classes abandon the constancy of internal temperature under certain conditions. On the other hand, various reptiles, fishes and even insects can, in the short term at least, achieve levels of heat production which yield body temperatures several degrees higher than the environment. Both of these exceptions to the two general categories are sometimes referred to as heterotherms (*heteros*, one or other), and we shall have to consider them further in Chapters 5 and 7. For the present, one thing should not escape our attention. This is that the development of ' endothermic homoiothermy ' represents for the animal an enormously important step towards what Joseph Barcroft (1872–1947) called ' a new freedom, by adapting not itself to the internal environment, but the internal environment to itself '.

1.2.2. *Temperature Compensation and Adaptation*

From what we have said about the various descriptive terms you will not be surprised to learn that poikilothermic animals were once believed to be completely the slaves of environmental temperature. Thus, it was thought that the metabolic rate of individuals of a given species must necessarily be slower in colder climates than in warm. A great deal of investigation has now shown this attitude to under-estimate the adaptability of the so-called cold-blooded animals, for what happens in nature is that a whole series of compensatory mechanisms are brought into play which adjust the body rates to the prevailing ambient temperature in such a way that metabolic intensities may be remarkably similar over a wide geographical range. Whereas the homoiotherm achieves its physiological independence by maintaining a relatively constant internal body temperature, the poikilotherm manages at least a limited degree of independence by adjusting its biochemical processes in accordance with external conditions. Both types of response are termed physiological compensation or adaptation, and they have been defined in a general way by C. L. Prosser as any functional property of an individual which favours continued successful living in an altered environment.

The compensations of the poikilotherm are often referred to as physiological conformity, whereas those of the homoiotherm are called physiological regulation. It is with the latter type of response that we are chiefly concerned in this book, although with both kinds two levels are usually recognized. The organism is said to tolerate the stresses imposed by normal fluctuations in environmental temperature and to

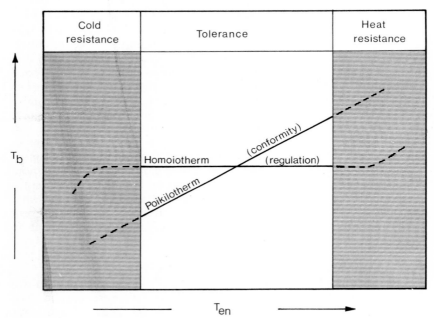

Fig. 1.3. Diagram showing the type of physiological compensation seen in the poikilotherm (conformity) and in the homoiotherm (regulation) in response to changes in the temperature of the environment.

resist the strains of abnormal ones (fig. 1.3). In the first situation ordinary body functions are maintained indefinitely, whereas the problems presented by the second can be withstood only for a period which depends on the severity of the change ; if prolonged, the new conditions cause damage, destruction and ultimately death. The ability of organisms to tolerate and resist changes of temperature is largely determined by their state of acclimatization, that is, their previous history of exposure to temperatures approximating to those encountered under stress. This subject is discussed in Chapter 7.

6

1.2.3. *The Concept of Homoiostasis*

Before we consider the physiology of homoiothermy in more detail it is worth pausing for a moment to recall the meaning of the more general term homoiostasis.

We have seen how the organism's power of adaptation to change implies that the animal and its external environment are best viewed as one whole. Within limits, the organism adjusts the composition of the fluid bathing its cells to compensate for fluctuations in the outside world. In the birds and mammals, a considerable stability of the internal environment has been achieved in the form, not only of constancy of temperature, but also of materials derived from the food, of water, oxygen and a host of other constituents and properties. It is the function of the autonomic nervous system to maintain this stability. Thus, it governs the constancy of body temperature, maintains the level of blood glucose and of blood pressure, controls the availability of food materials by its influence on the glands and muscles of the gut, guards the concentrations of oxygen, carbon dioxide and hydrogen ions in the blood by its regulation of respiration and, in short, preserves the optimum conditions in which the body's fundamental processes may operate. Walter Cannon (1871–1945), following the teaching of Claude Bernard (1813–78), gave the name homoiostasis to this condition of internal uniformity which is made possible by the adjustments of the organism to changes in its external environment.

The regulation of body temperature is perhaps the finest example there is of the integrative, homoiostatic action of the nervous system, since it involves so comprehensive a variety of physiological and behavioural responses.

1.2.4. *The Cost and Value of Temperature Independence*

It is usually argued that the advantage to the homoiotherm of maintaining a constant internal temperature lies in its greater freedom to exploit the external environment. By eliminating one of the most influential variables of the internal environment, and adopting a high and relatively stable temperature, the organism can sustain a level of both metabolic and locomotor activity and achieve a complexity of organization which would otherwise have been impossible. The effect of rising temperature on chemical reactions is, as we have seen, to increase their rate ; when we remember that the rise for a given increase in temperature will be different for different reactions, it is easy to see why a constant temperature throughout a complex organism would offer ideal conditions for the nervous co-ordination which is essential if complexity is to have any value. Nevertheless, this remains a largely speculative argument and undoubtedly the best evidence for the advantages of homoiothermy is to be seen in the dominance of present-day birds and mammals in conquering so wide a variety of the earth's

7

climatic conditions, particularly its colder regions. The complexity of organization and biological success enjoyed by the insects could not have been equalled, on land, by large animals without homoiothermy.

Although the value of homoiothermy may seem obvious, it is not always realized that the advantages are paid for at a high price. Despite the possession of efficient barriers to the loss of body heat in the form of fat, and of fur or feathers, heat dissipation is still rapid, especially as the internal body temperature is often many degrees above that of the environment. At least 80 per cent of the metabolic energy is used in maintaining thermal homoiostasis, and the need for a continuous high level of heat production imposes considerable limitations to the freedom of the homoiothermic animal, which must spend much of its time in the search for food. Indeed, so high is the price of homoiothermy that some animals, which are perfectly capable of maintaining a high and constant temperature in warm conditions, give up the expense altogether in cold weather or at night, thus reducing substantially the overall metabolic cost (see Chapter 5).

1.2.5. *The Level of the Regulated Temperature*

It is a curious fact that all species of mammals and birds which are truly homoiothermic maintain the temperature of their deep body tissues (brain, heart, viscera etc.) within the narrow range between 36 and 43°C. What is so special about this particular range of temperature and why was it selected rather than some other ?

To this question we can offer only tentative answers. For example, it is sometimes said that 37–38°C (the normal deep body temperature of man) is the optimum for the activity of many enzymes of physiological importance. Although this is quite correct, what is equally true is that other enzymes have optimum temperatures which are higher or lower than this, and in any case this hypothesis ignores the fact that the extremities of the body, where enzymes also function, are often at considerably lower temperatures than that of the deep body organs.

Another possibility is that 36–43°C represents a compromise between two unfavourable ranges, one higher and one lower. Selection of a lower temperature would not only reduce the rate of bodily chemical activities, but would also reduce the difference between body temperature and the average environmental temperature so that the physiological adjustments necessary to counter minor fluctuations in the latter would be relatively great. Alternatively, selection of a higher range would have been dangerously close to the point (43–47°C) at which heat-death could occur as a result of exercise or exposure to the sun.

A. C. Burton and O. G. Edholm have suggested that the level of the regulated temperature may well be connected with the automatic stability of the thermal steady state. A rise in the body temperature of a

8

poikilotherm would accelerate the rate of heat loss (if environmental temperature were unchanged) as well as that of heat production. They argue that physiological responses to changes of body temperature might be made most easily if both heat production and heat loss were increased equally by a given rise. The two would then remain in balance and the normal temperature would be restored by compensatory adjustments by the animal. By assuming the Q_{10} of metabolism to lie between 2·3 and 2·5, they calculate that the optimum stability of heat balance would occur at a body temperature between 35 and 38°C. By taking somewhat different values for the calculations this argument could be extended equally well to the body temperatures of birds which are generally 3–4 K above those of mammals.

1.2.6. *Evolution of Homoiothermy*

If we accept the theory of evolution by natural selection we must produce a plausible account of how the mechanisms employed by homoiotherms for internal body heating evolved in some way in animals whose ancestors did not possess them. The precise details can never be known, but evidence from the fossil record and more particularly from the temperature relations of living reptiles, birds and mammals, can provide us with the basis for at least a reasonable guess of how this evolution occurred.

Our knowledge of the origin of mammals is a great deal more detailed than that of the origin of birds, partly because of the far more extensive fossil record and partly because of the presence of certain surviving mammals whose morphology indicates that they probably diverged early from the main mammalian stock. The reptilian line that eventually gave rise to the mammals can be traced back as far as the Carboniferous, but the monotremes appeared first only in the early Jurassic, about 150 million years ago. Some 70 million years later the marsupials appeared, derived probably from a different group of mammal-like reptiles from that which gave rise to the monotremes. The earlier marsupials show marked similarities to the present-day opossums and also to the insectivores, the oldest of the placental mammals and the group from which all the others seem to have arisen. If you are interested in the story, the details of mammalian evolution can be found greatly expanded in any textbook of palaeontology, and this is in striking contrast to the sparse clues that we have on the birds. The earliest known bird, *Archaeopteryx lithographica* from the upper Jurassic, indicates that the class arose from a group near to the dinosaurs. (*Archaeopteryx* would itself be regarded as a reptile if it did not show evidence of perfect feathers.) Beyond that we know little, except that the development of a new type of vertebrate organization, such as we see in both mammals and birds, took an immense period of time, about 50 million years. This, though, is hardly surprising when we consider the complexity of the changes involved in acquiring and perfecting the mechanisms for internal body heating.

The development of endothermic homoiothermy was an exceptionally progressive step in evolution because it demanded an eight- to ten-fold increase in the metabolic rate. A sustained rise of this magnitude would have been impossible without some limitation to the loss of the heat generated, and it is probable that this was achieved first by the utilization of behaviour patterns which already existed in ectothermic forms. The consistently warm conditions that prevailed during the Triassic and Jurassic periods would have been especially favourable in this connexion, and it is significant that there are in the equatorial regions today (where ambient conditions most closely resemble those of the Triassic) several reptilian species which are capable of maintaining high, relatively constant body temperatures during their periods of activity, even though they possess only the normal poikilothermic rate of heat production. This is a good starting point from which to consider the possible origin of true endothermy.

Behavioural thermoregulation consists in keeping the body temperature fairly constant (within 3–4 K) by means of sheltering in the shade or basking in the sun in response to fluctuations above or below the optimum temperature for the species. The important point here is that this ability implies a sensitivity to changes in the body temperature rather similar to that which has been extensively investigated in mammals (Chapter 6). In this class, as well as in birds, a small area at the base of the forebrain called the hypothalamus is responsible for detecting fluctuations in internal temperature and for organizing the appropriate protective responses. It has long been known that reptiles, amphibians, and even fish, as well as homoiotherms, are capable of selecting thermal preferences in a variable environment, and it has recently been shown in all these animals that it is the temperature of the brain which is important. If this is altered experimentally to the extent that it would be by exposure to an external temperature harmful to the animal, the creature responds in the same way as if it were actually exposed to that environment. Further evidence from neurophysiology indicates that the nerve cells most sensitive to these alterations lie in the hypothalamus.

The evolutionary significance of these findings is that they suggest that hypothalamic temperature-sensitivity may be an ancient property which existed before the emergence of homoiothermic animals. Large daily and seasonal fluctuations in body temperature would first have been suffered by the early amphibians dwelling in shallow water, and the job of the hypothalamus may first have been to organize the necessary thermal compensations in the vital metabolic processes so as to permit a co-ordination of function which was essential for the animal's survival. It is possible that this initial stage of physiological conformity may, as

10

the rate of heat production increased during the evolution of endothermy, have become adapted to serve the regulation of a constant body
temperature. Indeed, it may be that the development of some kind of
thermostat to prevent over-heating became a condition of survival,
much as it was in the case of the early motor car.

It is to the mammalian line that we must turn for clues on the origin
of endothermy proper, and in this connexion Sir Charles Martin's
classical study (1903) on the Australian monotremes and marsupials is
an object lesson in itself. When he compared the body temperatures

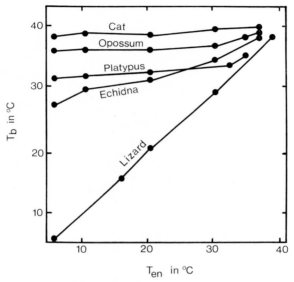

Fig. 1.4. Variations of body temperature in a reptile (lizard), the monotremes
(echidna and platypus), a marsupial (opossum) and a placental mammal
(cat) caused by exposure for two hours to environmental temperatures
between 5 and 40°C. (Redrawn from Martin, *Lancet*, 1930.)

of various animals at an air temperature of 15°C he found a graded
series, increasing from the monotremes to the marsupials and finally to
the placental mammals. The variation of body temperature which
resulted from exposure to a wide range of ambient temperatures was
also greatest (among the mammals) in the monotremes (fig. 1.4).

When the metabolic rates of his various mammalian species were
examined at different temperatures it was found that minimum heat
production always occurred at about 30°C. The basal rate of the
monotremes and marsupials was only about one-third that of the higher
mammals, while the most interesting thing of all was that the extent of

the metabolic response to falling air temperature decreased in the order echidna, platypus, marsupials and finally placental mammals. That is, the lower the level of development of homoiothermy the more marked was the metabolic response to cold ; this is shown in a qualitative way in fig 1.5. Finally, since exposure to high temperatures caused a greater rise in the body temperature of the monotremes than of the marsupials and placentals, the latter animals apparently had better-developed mechanisms for increasing the loss of heat.

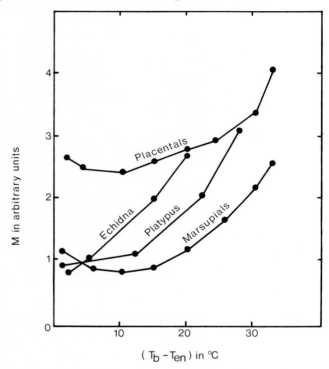

Fig. 1.5. Metabolic rates of the monotremes, marsupials and placental mammals plotted against the difference in temperature between animal and environment (T_b-T_{en}). The curves represent the results of a number of experiments on several animals of each kind. (Redrawn from Martin, *Phil. Trans. R. Soc.*, 1903.)

More recent work has confirmed Martin's own conclusion that the study of temperature relations in the primitive mammals shows that variation of the rate of heat production is probably the ancestral method of physiological temperature regulation. During the evolution of homoiothermy the development of mechanisms for increasing metabolism in accordance with the rate of physical heat loss freed the early endotherms from dependence on the external temperature and permitted greater exploration of cold climates. But this method of regulation had serious limitations in that high ambient temperatures could still cause an explosive rise in the temperature of the body ; although this might have been detected by the hypothalamic thermostat, the simple behavioural responses available would not have been an adequate long-term solution for all animals.

The next step was the development of the ability to regulate the rate of heat loss. If, as is generally believed, this occurred at a time when considerable quantities of heat were already available to the highly active emerging homoiotherms (in which insulative protection was presumably also evolving in the shape of hair or feathers), it is probable that the cardiovascular system had been increased in efficiency to a point where it was pre-adapted for use in controlling the loss of heat ; as a variable and rapid transport system it could equally well restrict the heat of metabolism to the deep parts of the body to maintain warmth, or carry any excess to the surface for dissipation. Some of this heat could also be lost by evaporating water at the surface and in this connexion it is interesting that the platypus, which possesses a limited number of sweat glands on the snout, is somewhat more successful at tolerating high temperatures than is the echidna, which has none. The marsupials are more efficient still because they can evaporate water in the form of saliva, by licking the coat and by panting. Finally, in the placental mammals we see the increasing dominance of heat loss in the regulation of body temperature ; the means include active and highly sensitive changes in insulation as well as the full development of the sweating mechanism. In man this type of response is so sophisticated that the importance of metabolic changes in thermoregulation is reduced to a minimum.

We might add two words of caution before leaving the subject of evolution. First, when considering data like those of Martin we should not forget that his observations were made under laboratory conditions that were excellent for physiological measurements but which virtually eliminated the behavioural adjustments that animals make in nature. This interference would have a particularly drastic impact on the performance of those animals which rely principally on the behavioural responses. Therefore when we see that the platypus regulated its temperature efficiently between 5 and 30°C but suffered a rapid collapse above this range, we should not conclude at once that it is an unsuccessful homoiotherm. In its natural habitat the platypus avoids such thermal stress by returning to water where much more heat can be lost by conduction.

Second, we should be wary of concluding too quickly that a relatively low or unstable body temperature need necessarily be a primitive characteristic. These phenomena may equally well be indicative of

13

specialization to a particular set of environmental conditions. The work of K. Schmidt-Nielsen, for example, has shown that the camel tolerates wide fluctuations of its body temperature not because it is unsuccessful in coping with the desert climate but as a supremely successful adaptation that conserves the water that would otherwise be expended to maintain thermal homoiostasis (Chapter 7).

1.3. *THE LIMITATIONS OF HOMOIOTHERMY*

The term ' body temperature ' is a misleading one because it implies some average temperature which in reality cannot be measured. We are all aware from common experience that different parts of our bodies (notably the hands and feet) can be at very different temperatures at one and the same time, and this is simply because some sites in the body are subject to widely varying conditions of heat production and heat loss. In clinical medicine, man's body temperature is usually measured by a mercury thermometer in the mouth, occasionally under the arm or in the fold of the groin. In experiments on man, the rectum has been the most widely used site, although in recent years there has been a strong swing in favour of the temperature of the tympanic membrane, which can be readily sensed by a thermocouple inserted into the external auditory canal ; this is the closest we can get to the human hypothalamus.

Experiments on animals are not subject to the same restrictions as those on man, and temperature-sensing devices such as miniature thermistors or thermocouples can be surgically implanted under anaesthesia into any organ of the body and comparisons thus made between a variety of sites. There is no need for us to study these differences in any detail, but it is important to realize that the body is not thermally homogeneous ; it is characterized by substantial thermal gradients, not only from the deep organs to the cooler skin, but also between the organs themselves. In man, oral temperature is consistently below that of the rectum, usually by about 0·5 K, while tympanic membrane temperature is a good deal less stable than either of these and subject to fluctuations of up to 1·0 K in either direction during rapidly changing conditions.

1.3.1. *Diurnal Rhythm*

One of the most fundamental attributes of organisms appears to be the way in which many of their functions and activities undergo rhythmic changes which correspond to the temporal characteristics of the environment. The four major periodicities of nature, namely the seasons, the phases of the moon, the tides, and the light–dark cycle, are all represented in animals, but for our purpose it will be sufficient to consider only the influence of the last and best understood of these.

The period of the earth's rotation, and the resulting alternation between day and night, is reflected in animals as physiological variations of approximately 24 hours duration. These are known as circadian rhythms (*circa*, about ; *dies*, day). The fluctuations in the deep body temperature of homoiotherms are typically of the order of 1 K, the maxima and minima coming in the day or night according to whether the animal is diurnal or nocturnal in activity. Surprisingly, however, removal from the influence of the natural day–night cycle does not eliminate the rhythm, although shifts of phase may result, for example, from long-distance and rapid journeys by air. Furthermore, the normal pattern for an animal can usually be reversed by inversion of the light–dark regime.

Other variables related to temperature regulation also show circadian rhythms, including metabolic rate and food intake, heart rate, blood flow and locomotor activity. It is often stated that the rhythms of body temperature and oxygen consumption are the result of those in activity and feeding, but it now appears that this may be an over-simplification. Likewise, the relationship between metabolism and body temperature may not be causal ; they may equally well be oscillating in response to separate, though similar, stimuli or timekeepers.

1.3.2. *Regional Heterothermy : the Core and the Shell*

The differences in temperature between various of the deep organs of the body are small enough to justify the concept of one particular ' core ' or deep body temperature (that is, of the deep-lying tissues of the head, neck and trunk), whose fluctuations as a whole are no greater than those between its different parts. The rest of the body according to this idea forms the ' shell ', the temperature of which varies over a considerable range according to ambient conditions, metabolic load and various other physiological factors. The shell consists of the coat of hair, feathers or clothing, the skin and superficial tissues over the whole body, and all the tissues of the limbs (fig. 1.6) ; it is characterized by steep thermal gradients and a lability of up to 35 K. Clearly, the constancy of body temperature which is almost a definition of homoiothermy cannot be said to apply to the tissues of the shell. This is an important consideration because direct measurements show that the variable shell of the trunk in man is some 20–30 mm thick, and calculations on this basis indicate that more than 50 per cent of the body must thus be designated.

The core–shell concept is obviously an over-simplification, but it is useful if it reminds us that, to a very large degree, the constancy of the core temperature is guaranteed only at the expense of substantial changes in the temperature of the shell, which therefore acts as a heat capacitor to protect the core. If normal thermoregulation is to be maintained in hot conditions the skin temperature must be kept at least 1 K below that of

15

the core, otherwise the transfer of surplus heat to the environment becomes impossible and core temperature is bound to rise. If the skin temperature should exceed core temperature then the core will continually gain heat and a state of distress will follow. Conversely, in cold climates, skin temperature may be allowed to fall to near the freezing

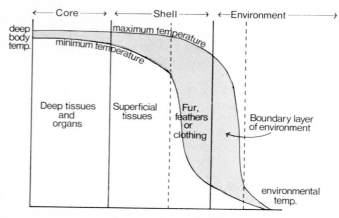

Fig. 1.6. Diagram showing the thermal gradient from the core of the body through the shell to the environment. The deep body temperature is maintained physically by varying the insulation of the shell. The boundary layer of the environment is of relatively still air close to the body surface. An indication of the thermal variability at each level is given by the width of the shaded area.

point of water, greatly reducing the flow of heat from the body surface to the environment. We shall see in Chapter 4 that under such extremes the peripheral tissues display special mechanisms to prevent damage and to minimize heat loss from the core.

1.3.3. *What Temperature is Regulated ?*

If the protective role of the superficial tissues involves them in wide fluctuations of temperature, it is obvious that the body shell cannot be the site of the actual ' regulated temperature '. This naturally prompts the question of whether we should, indeed, expect the regulated temperature to reside at a fixed location in the body. Is it not equally probable that some more subtle ' average body temperature ' might fit rather better the requirement of constancy (implying regulation) under varying thermal loads ?

As so often happens in science, it is now thought likely, in one important sense at least, that both of these are partially true. While it is not doubted that the temperature of all the core tissues is in some way involved in the regulated temperature, there is now a great deal of experimental evidence to suggest that it is actually the hypothalamic temperature which is most closely guarded, and that this must somehow reflect the thermal conditions of the core as a whole. The shell temperature also influences the hypothalamus, sometimes by modulating its sensitivity to changes in the core, but sometimes by a more direct action. The hypothalamus, like any other part of the nervous system, can operate only with messages specially coded in the form of minute electrical impulses and thermal information must be transduced before it has any significance. Recent experiments that have demonstrated the direct influence of temperature changes on the pattern of neural impulses in the hypothalamus, as distinct from any other structure in the brain, represent some of the most elegant evidence in support of the contention that the hypothalamus has a uniquely important role in the regulation of body temperature.

Whatever the regulated temperature, modern ideas of the operation of the regulating system indicate that it is really the magnitude of the difference between this temperature and a ' set ' or reference temperature which activates the regulating responses to maintain constancy. The hypothalamus is, once again, the part of the nervous system most likely to possess the capability of comparing its own temperature with a set reference and of initiating changes in heat production and heat loss such as to reduce the difference and thus return the regulated temperature to normal. Other nervous structures can influence the thermoregulatory responses of the body but none has been shown actually capable of regulating the body's internal temperature (Chapter 6).

1.3.4. *Failures of Homoiothermy*

One of the prices paid for the functional benefits of homoiothermy is the high metabolic rate that is necessary. Another is that the core temperature must be maintained within quite narrow limits, for the deep organs and tissues have apparently become so specialized that they can operate satisfactorily only within this range. Thus any fluctuations of ambient temperature substantially beyond the level to which an animal is accustomed may place a strain on the thermoregulatory mechanisms which is greater than they can bear. Such is the efficiency of the mechanisms that the ambient range is often impressively wide, especially in man where it is further extended by the use of clothes and shelter. But the range of internal temperature over which the maintenance of self-regulating homoiothermy can continue is seldom more than 10 K. At the lower extreme, death typically occurs at a temperature well above the minimum level that the animal can tolerate, apparently because spontaneous re-warming in the form of metabolic acceleration has become impossible, rather than as a result of circulatory or respiratory failure. The upper extreme is fatal because an increase in the tissue temperature accelerates heat production according to the van't Hoff law, and normal control becomes inadequate to cope with the consequent effects of a vicious cycle.

1.3.5. *Periodic Heterothermy : Hibernation and Torpor*

The typical homoiotherm has no choice in severely cold weather but to attempt to maintain its normal internal temperature by mobilizing all the metabolic resources available. If the attempt fails it will die.

The hibernating mammals, however, respond to such conditions by allowing the body temperature to fall almost to that of the air ; this greatly diminishes the metabolic rate and consequently its drain on a limited supply of food (Chapter 5). Others, notably some of the bears, are often considered not to be genuine hibernators because, although they respond to the cold winter weather by sleeping for much of the time, the deep body temperature falls by only a few degrees and arousal from sleep occurs quite easily. The true hibernators become virtually poikilothermic during their winter sleep, the body temperature fluctuating passively with the environment. An important distinction from the obligatory dormancy or cold narcosis of poikilotherms, however, is that hibernating homoiotherms have an extraordinary capacity for rapidly generating heat from their reserves of fat when the ambient temperature rises, or when it falls so low as to threaten the freezing of the tissues. In response to such a stimulus the temperature regulating system is able to elicit complete or partial arousal—hibernation is therefore not a real failure of the system—whereas in the poikilotherm (or, indeed, in non-hibernating homoiotherms) there is no comparable ability.

Bats differ from other hibernators in that they do not restrict their periods of torpor to the winter ; even in summer, when they are resting during the day, their body temperature falls to near that of the air. Similar behaviour has been observed in swifts during bad weather when there are no flying insects, and in certain hummingbirds which always become torpid after dark.

Prolonged torpor also occurs in some mammals and birds at high ambient temperature, when the condition is called aestivation. It again appears that energy conservation is the biological objective, and extreme aridity and the consequent threat of water deprivation the usual stimulus.

1.4. *CHEMICAL AND PHYSICAL THERMOREGULATION*

1.4.1. *Body Temperature, Energy Metabolism and Heat Loss*

You will remember that, in the poikilotherm, body temperature varies linearly and energy metabolism exponentially with ambient temperature. The emancipation of the homoiotherm from environmental temperature is the result of its achieving a delicate balance between the mechanisms of heat production and those for heat loss (fig. 1.7). Thus, as the thermal load is increased so the energy metabolism decreases, and vice versa. The ability to increase the heat production in the cold to three or four times the minimum rate, chiefly by hormonal means and by shivering,

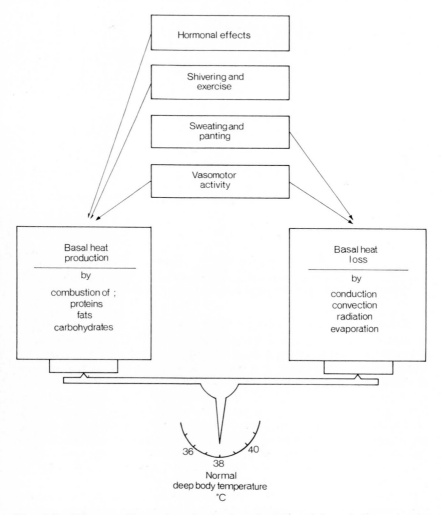

Fig. 1.7. Diagram illustrating the basic principles of heat balance in the homoiotherm. The normal deep body temperature is the dynamic resultant of chemical heat production and physical heat loss as they are affected by physiological factors.

was long ago termed by Max Rubner (1854–1932) the chemical regulation of body temperature, an expression which emphasizes that the production of heat is ultimately from the chemical breakdown of foodstuffs.

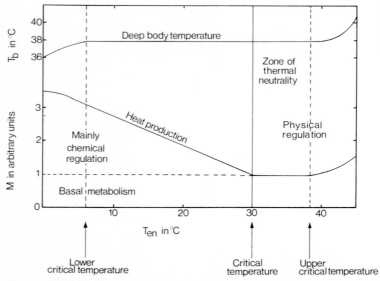

Fig. 1.8. The relation between deep body temperature, metabolic heat production and environmental temperature in a typical homoiotherm.

If the environment is warmed, heat production typically reaches its minimum level (basal metabolism) at about 30°C air temperature. When the temperature rises above this point there is at first no change in metabolism and the range over which this remains so is called the zone of thermoneutrality. Throughout this zone, and above it, the homoiotherm engages in what Rubner described as physical regulation. This form of control consists in the alteration of the effective conductivity, or the insulation of the body, a control which is exercised by varying the amount of blood flowing to the periphery and by influencing the rate at which water is evaporated from the skin and respiratory tract. The physical channels of heat loss are thus enhanced in efficiency by physiological means.

At the upper end of the zone of thermoneutrality the physical mechanisms eventually become inadequate, so that the body temperature begins to rise, causing a secondary increase in metabolism. The levels of environmental temperature associated with increased heat production, at the lower and the upper end of the thermoneutral zone, have been

20

variously named ; we shall refer to them simply as the critical temperature and the upper critical temperature respectively.

Physical regulation does not operate only in neutral or warm conditions. In the cold, the withdrawal of blood from the superficial tissues and the erection of fur or feathers reduces the physical transfer of heat to the environment, but since these effects usually reach their maximum fairly soon after temperature drops below the zone of thermoneutrality, acute cold conditions are countered primarily by increased metabolism. Ultimately, if the ambient temperature continues to fall, a point is reached where the high rate of heat production can no longer keep pace with the rapid rate of heat loss ; thus, at what is called the lower critical temperature, there is a fall in the temperature of the body core. However, the success of the homoiothermic animals in tolerating so wide a range of environmental temperature is very largely attributable to their ability to combine the two methods of regulation, the chemical control of heat production and the physical control of heat loss. The relations between body temperature, energy metabolism and ambient temperature are summarized in fig. 1.8.

CHAPTER 2

 physical heat exchange

2.1. *HEAT TRANSFER AND INSULATION*

In some respects the machinery of the body is like a thermodynamic engine which transforms energy from one kind to another. A fraction of the chemical energy derived from the breakdown of food is converted into work, but because of the body's limited efficiency the greater part appears finally as heat. In the homoiothermic animal a balance is maintained between the rate at which this heat is lost to the environment and the rate at which it is produced by metabolism, so that the resulting constancy of temperature reflects a thermal steady state with a continuous flow of energy through the system. Both sides of the equation of heat balance, namely the heat production and the heat loss, are variable, and in practice the total heat content, or heat storage, of the body may fluctuate somewhat according to both physical and physiological conditions.

In the cold a thermal steady state is attainable only if the body is capable of generating sufficient heat to counteract the rapid physical transfer to the environment which still continues even when all the physiological barriers to heat flow are maximal. In hot conditions, the environment must be capable of accepting the body's metabolic heat without requiring a rise in body temperature above physiological limits. The transfer of heat by conduction, convection and radiation (referred to as direct transfer) which normally occurs from the body surface to the environment becomes impossible when the temperature difference between them disappears, although transfer in the form of the heat of vaporization (indirect transfer) continues so long as the environment can take up water vapour. A simple qualitative picture of the overall energy exchanges between a homoiotherm and its environment is given in figure 2.1.

2.1.1. *The Laws of Heat Flow*

2.1.1.1. *General equations*

The heat balance of the body at rest can be expressed in the simple equation :

$$M = H_L + S$$

where M is the rate of metabolic heat production, H_L is the overall rate of heat loss, and S is the rate of heat storage. S is positive for a net heat

22

gain by the body, negative for a loss, and zero when the body is in thermal equilibrium.

Since the body loses heat to the environment by evaporation (E) and exchanges it in both directions by conduction (K), convection (C) and

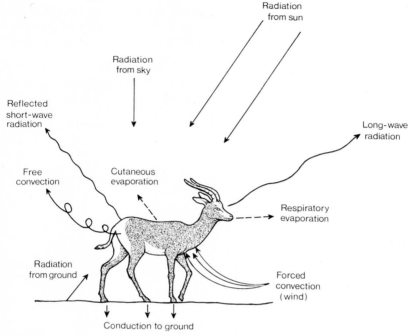

Fig. 2.1. Diagram of the principal energy exchanges between a homoiotherm and its environment. The heat produced by metabolism is lost under most conditions chiefly by radiation and convection. In hot conditions the natural evaporation of water is accelerated by physiological means.

radiation (R), the overall transfer will be the algebraic sum of the individual components and the full equation of heat balance can then be written:

$$M = E + K + C + R + S.$$

The terms E, K, C and R will be positive for a net loss of heat, negative for a gain. All of the terms in the equation must be expressed in the same units for energy rate (watts in SI) and because the body's energy exchange is always related to its surface area, the unit for each symbol is watt per square metre.

That is, we can imagine a person sitting unclad in surroundings at about 39°C, when he could be gaining heat by conduction (K negative),

23

convection (C negative) and radiation (R negative), while still losing heat by evaporation (E positive).

2.1.1.2. *Newton's law of cooling*

When Sir Isaac Newton (1643–1727) investigated the fall in temperature of a hot physical body in a cool environment, he found that cooling occurred at a rate proportional to the difference in temperature between the body and its surroundings* (fig. 2.2). In its simplest form :

$$T_L = k(T_b - T_{en})$$

where T_L is the rate of loss of temperature, T_b the temperature of the body, T_{en} the temperature of the environment, and k is the so-called

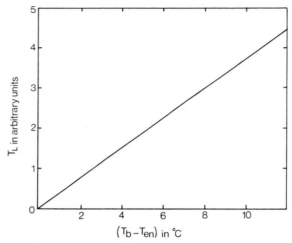

Fig. 2.2. Newton's law of cooling. The rate of loss of temperature (T_L) is proportional to the excess temperature of a body over its environment. Essentially the same relations hold for the rate of loss of heat from a body of constant temperature.

cooling constant (equivalent to the thermal conductivity) which depends upon the material of the body, and on the ratio of its mass to surface area, although not on the two temperatures. If there is no heat production, as in Newton's experiments, the heat loss leads to a decrease in temperature, the rate of which falls off exponentially as the temperature of the body approaches that of the environment. Thus, whereas Newton was interested in the loss of temperature from his

* The law holds approximately, for small temperature differences, in still air ; for ventilated cooling in a draught of air it is followed closely over larger ranges.

inanimate objects, in studying the homoiotherm we are concerned more with the loss of heat from a body whose temperature remains unchanged. Despite this discrepancy, Newton's law still applies quite well to the physiological situation. If we modify the law for application to an animal, however, we consider the rate of loss of heat from the surface and thus wish to know the area of the surface (A), its average temperature (T_{su}) and the thermal conductivity of the surface layer (k'):

$$H_L = k'A(T_{su} - T_{en}).$$

2.1.1.3. Fourier's law

If the body is in a steady state, the rate of loss of heat from the surface must be equal to the rate at which heat is passing through the shell from the core to the surface. By Fourier's law the rate of loss will be inversely proportional to the thickness of the shell (d) and directly proportional to its thermal conductivity (k'), to the difference in temperature between the body core (T_{co}) and surface (T_{su}), and to the surface area (A):

$$H_L = k'\frac{A}{d}(T_{co} - T_{su}).$$

2.1.1.4. Body size and rates of cooling

If for a moment we consider the dead animal body as distinct from the living, we shall be able to see how the effect of body size on the rate of loss of temperature is rather different from that on the rate of loss of heat. Fourier's law states that the rate of loss of heat is proportional to the surface area, but the surface area is roughly proportional to $m^{2/3}$ (where m is mass, commonly called body-weight), whereas the heat capacity of a body is proportional to the mass itself. Therefore, the rate of cooling of a body will be proportional to $m^{2/3}/m = m^{-1/3}$; since m is proportional to l^3, where l is the linear dimension, as the 'size' of the body decreases, its rate of loss of heat will increase, since it is inversely proportional to the 'size' as represented by l.

The importance of this relationship for the study of temperature regulation is in the implication that the rate of metabolic heat production per unit mass in small homoiotherms must be greater than in large ones if a constant body temperature is to be maintained (see Chapter 3). In a very general way we might say that whereas the problem for the small animal is that of producing sufficient heat to counteract the rapid physical losses, with very large animals there is more likely to be difficulty in dissipating the heat at a sufficiently rapid rate, simply because their metabolic heat production is so great in relation to the ratio of surface area to volume.

2.1.2. Conductance and the Insulation of Tissues, Coat and Air

In any animal that is maintaining a constant body temperature it follows that :

Rate of metabolic heat production $(M)=$
Rate of heat loss $(H_L) = k'A(T_{su} - T_{en})$.

If we treat the surface area as unchanging (which is not quite the case for the ' effective ' area because of postural alterations on the part of the animal—see Section 2.1.2.6) then we have a simple definition of thermal conductivity in terms of metabolism and the temperature gradient from the surface to the environment :

$$k'' = \frac{M}{(T_{su} - T_{en})}$$

where k'' is the thermal conductivity per unit area. For the body tissues k'' is not a constant, because the rate of cooling can be altered, especially in the thermoneutral zone, by physical regulation of the superficial blood flow and by changes in the thickness of the coat. It is by such means as this that the metabolism can remain unchanged despite a degree of alteration in the temperature gradient, although below the critical temperature the value of k'' does rapidly reach a minimum and a further cooling of the environment would mean that the equation could be balanced only by increasing heat production.

2.1.2.1. Tissue conductance and thermal gradients

Physiologists (and, we might say, most animals also) are usually less concerned with rates of heat flow from the body core to the environment than with ways of reducing the flow, so that it is convenient to express Fourier's law in terms of resistance to cooling :

$$H_L = A \frac{(T_{co} - T_{su})}{I}$$

where I is the resistance to heat flow per unit area (d/k'), known as the specific insulation of the animal.

By using the factor I in our expression of Fourier's law we have an equation which is analogous to Ohm's law :

$$C = \frac{V}{R}$$

where C is current, V is electrical potential difference and R is resistance. In the case of heat flow, the temperature gradient corresponds to potential gradient, the rate of heat loss to current and the thermal insulation to electrical resistance. The reason why this is a more useful form of the equation is that we have to deal with layers of insulation in series far more often than in parallel ; in such cases the total insulation is then calculated simply as the sum of the individual insulations. If we continued to use thermal conductivity in our calculations we should have to invert the individual values, sum the reciprocals, and invert again, just as in the summation of electrical resistances in parallel.

The concept of insulation of the tissues is not concerned with heat lost by evaporation since this occurs external to the skin and is governed by different laws (see Section 2.2.4) ; we therefore have to consider only the direct transfer. However, there is another problem in connexion with the animal's specific insulation because this property is affected by various factors, including changes in the fur, feathers or clothing, which influence an important part of the total insulation beyond the skin itself. To minimize this difficulty it is customary to think of the specific insulation as consisting of two parts, one from the core to the skin (internal) and another from the skin to the environment (external). In animals which depend very little on evaporative heat loss from the skin, the internal and external heat flows will be similar, but in actively sweating animals they may be widely different because the heat that is carried to the skin by direct transfer only is then lost to the environment by a combination of both direct and indirect methods. In either case, the distinction between the two components is useful when making calculations of specific insulation, and it also reminds us of the importance of purely physical factors, like air movement and humidity, in governing the loss of heat through the external part.

In passing it is worth noting that the two components of specific insulation can equally well be described in terms of thermal gradients. That from the core to the skin would be the physiological gradient and that from the skin to the environment the physical gradient. The flow of heat, in either case, depends on the magnitude of the respective temperature differences. In man, for example, the average skin temperature in comfortable conditions is 5 K below core temperature, maintaining a gradient between the two of about 0.2 K mm^{-1}. This condition permits the steady flow of heat from the core to the skin by conduction and convection and its dissipation to the air largely by convection and radiation ; there is a thermal steady state such that core temperature remains constant.

2.1.2.2. *Insulation of the tissues*

The insulation provided by the tissues themselves is theoretically dependent on the average thermal conductivity of the flesh down the core-to-skin gradient, a value which is essentially a function of the dead tissue. The heat flow by conduction (H_k) would be given by:

$$H_k = k''(T_{co} - T_{su})/d.$$

In practice, of course, the value of k'' varies with the type of tissue, and for our purpose it is sufficient to know that the conductivities of dead fat, skin and muscle are approximately in the ratio $1 : 2 : 3$; this is why a subcutaneous layer of fat or blubber is a highly efficient barrier to the flow of heat.

In the living animal, tissue insulation is also dependent on the ' convective ' transfer of heat to the skin through the bloodstream, and variations in blood flow to the superficial tissues represent the major way in which tissue insulation is altered. The heat flow by this form of convection (H_c) would be given by:

$$H_c = Q_{sk}\, c\, (T_{ar} - T_{ve})$$

where Q_{sk} is the blood flow to the skin, c is the specific heat capacity of the blood, and T_{ar} and T_{ve} the temperature respectively of the arterial blood leaving and the venous blood entering the core. An increase in flow not only brings more heat to the surface by convection, but also enhances the rate of conductive transfer from the core directly through the tissues to the skin. (Since the effect raises the skin temperature, heat losses to the environment by convection and radiation then also increase.) Blood flow to the skin can often be varied by a factor of more than a hundred, and the influence that this has on the insulation of thermal pathways from the core to the various parts of the body surface has been usefully expressed in terms of a ' thermal circulation index ' (Burton), which is the ratio of the external to the internal component of specific insulation. Thus:

$$\frac{I_{ex}}{I_{in}} = \frac{T_{sk} - T_{en}}{T_{co} - T_{sk}}$$

where I_{ex} and I_{in} are the external and internal insulations and T_{en}, T_{co} and T_{sk} the temperatures of the environment, the body core and the skin respectively.

The index can be used to show that the extremities of the body are the principal sites of physical thermoregulation. For example, in the domestic fowl, the thermal circulation index for the naked skin of the legs, feet and head increases by 5–15 fold between about 25 and 35°C ambient temperature, while that for the feathered skin over the rest of the body is almost unchanged (fig. 2.3).

2.1.2.3. *Insulation of the coat and air*

In mammals and birds with a thick covering of fur or feathers, as well as in man wearing heavy clothing, the coat external to the skin is often the chief factor in specific insulation. The thermal insulation of the

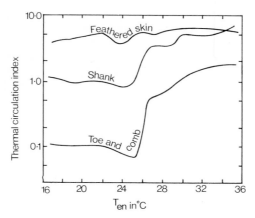

Fig. 2.3. The effect of environmental temperature on the thermal circulation index for feathered and unfeathered skin in the domestic fowl. (Redrawn from Richards, *J. Physiol.*, 1971.)

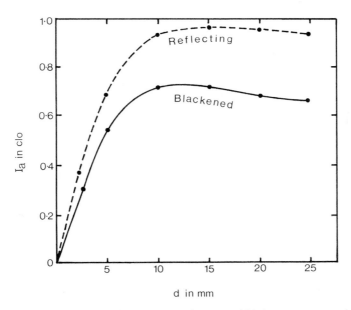

Fig. 2.4. The insulation of an empty air space (I_a) between two plates in relation to thickness (d). When radiation exchange is minimized by using reflecting plates, insulation is increased by about 40 per cent but the shape of the curve is unchanged. (Redrawn from Burton and Edholm, *Man in a Cold Environment*, 1955.)

29

coat is proportional to the thickness of the layer of still air that it can retain, but the insulation of an empty air space increases with thickness only up to a maximum of about 10 mm, after which convective currents of air begin to counteract the effect of width (fig. 2.4). With animal fur or the fabric of clothing the insulation depends on how well the hairs or fibres prevent such currents. Provided that the bulk density of the stabilizing material is low, the insulation is then once again proportional to thickness. The most effective fabrics are thus the ones which best maintain their thickness under all conditions, hence the value of a resilient or spongy texture.

The significance of the seasonal variations which occur in the effective insulation of animals' coats has been demonstrated in terms of alterations in the critical temperature. For the Alaskan red fox (*Vulpes fulva*) this is $-13°C$ in winter but only $7°C$ in summer when the fur is much thinner. By contrast, the critical temperature of the American red squirrel (*Tamiasciurus hudsonicus*), in which there is no seasonal change in the fur, is about $20°C$ all the year round. In unclothed man, the maintenance of homoiothermy would certainly not be possible at much below $0°C$, although the use of suitable protective clothing has made even the Antarctic accessible.

2.1.2.4. *The clo unit*

Traditionally, insulation was always measured in the old units of $m^2 hr °C kcal^{-1}$. Thirty years ago, however, a group of American physiologists introduced into human physiology a unit of insulation called the ' clo ' (from ' clothing '), in an attempt to convey a simpler, more direct, understanding of a difficult subject. Their concept is now widely used, especially since the clo unit is, of course, readily convertible into more conventional terms.

The heat lost by direct transfer down the external gradient from skin surface to environment can be expressed by Newton's law if the thermal conductivity (the inverse of insulation) is taken as that of the clothing together with that of the layer of still air which, even in the absence of clothing, envelops the body. The total external insulation (I_{ex}) would then be equal to the sum of the insulations of the clothing (I_{cl}) and of the air (I_a). The insulation of the clothing alone would be given by :

$$I_{cl} = \frac{T_{sk} - T_a}{H_L} - I_a$$

where H_L is the rate of heat loss by conduction, convection and radiation, T_a is the temperature of the air and T_{sk} the skin temperature.

Now the clo unit of insulation may be visualized simply as that necessary to keep the average man comfortable in an averagely warm environment ; it is sometimes conveniently described as the insulation provided by an ordinary business suit with underclothing. The rate of

30

heat loss of the average man under these conditions may be taken to be about 60 W m^{-2}, and under comfortable conditions about a quarter of this is in the form of evaporation (by insensible perspiration, not by sweating—see Chapter 4), leaving 45 W m^{-2} by direct transfer. The average environment is taken as 21°C and the average skin temperature as 33°C. Substituting in the formula :

$$I_{cl} = \frac{33 - 21}{45} - I_a = 0.27 - I_a.$$

On the basis of experimental findings the value of I_a is considered to be 0·12 K m^2 W^{-1} so that, finally, we have the value of I_{cl} alone as 0·15 K m^2 W^{-1}. This is equivalent to one clo unit.

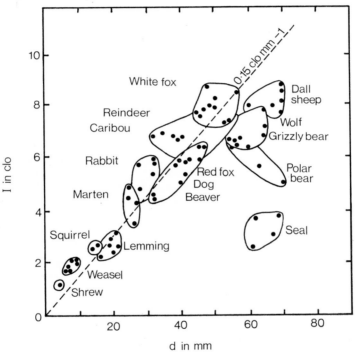

Fig. 2.5. Insulation (I) of fur in relation to thickness in a series of Arctic mammals. (Redrawn and modified from Scholander *et al.*, *Biol. Bull.*, 1950.)

The best insulation attained in practice with clothing is about 0·16 clo mm^{-1}, compared to 0·18 clo mm^{-1} for the insulation of motionless air. The fur of arctic animals compares quite favourably with this; if different species are compared, the relation of insulation to thickness is approximately linear with a slope of about 0·15 clo mm^{-1} (fig. 2.5).

31

Before leaving the subject of insulation of the coat we should not forget that in some cases the possession of fur or the wearing of suitable clothes may have protective value in hot conditions, notably in the presence of intense solar radiation. By reducing the heat load, such an insulating layer can, in the unshorn sheep for instance, have an effect which is readily measurable in terms of the diminished need for the costly evaporation of water.

2.1.2.5. *The effect of air movement and moisture*
In describing the clo unit we should, strictly speaking, include among the environmental conditions a rate of air movement of $0{\cdot}1$ m s^{-1} and a relative humidity of less than 50 per cent. Although we need not dwell on the more detailed considerations, experience tells us that when clothing is subject to a strong wind, or when it is damp, there is a considerable decrease in its insulating properties. We have seen that it is the still air trapped by the fur or clothing that provides the insulation, so it is not surprising that disruption of this stillness causes a decline in insulating ability. At low temperatures this effect may be serious when the disruption is due to a strong wind, but when caused by movements of the body itself (the ' internal wind ') it is commonly of value, in the cold as well as the heat, by allowing an increase in heat loss during exercise while metabolism is temporarily increased.

The effect of moisture in reducing insulation involves the ability of different fabrics to absorb or transmit the water evaporated from the skin surface. If considerable quantities of this water are taken up after sweating, the specific latent heat of vaporization lost by the body is retained by the clothing. The actual net loss of heat which follows may then be substantially less than that predicted on the basis of the quantity of water evaporated from the skin, the degree of reduction depending largely upon the ability of the fabric to transfer moisture from one layer to another by a process of capillarity. Of course, when liquid water itself is present the insulation is reduced as a result of an increase in heat capacity of some 3000 times, and in thermal conductivity of about 240 times. Substantial deposits of water (or even ice in severe climates) in clothing which does not ' breathe ' cause at best a chill feeling of discomfort when the period of exercise is over, and at worst can accelerate the rate of loss of heat to a serious degree.

Aquatic mammals such as otters and many seals, and probably all aquatic birds, have coats of dense fur or feathers close to the skin which entrap air. The insulation of the coat depends upon the degree of its waterproofing, and prior to the development of this property in young animals the coat actually offers very little protection.

2.1.2.6. *Overall insulation*
In considering the various superficial layers of the animal's body we

have been concerned with the factors which affect the insulation per unit area. What in practice determines the total non-evaporative heat transfer between the animal and its surroundings, however, is its overall insulation, which represents an integration of both behavioural and physiological responses. Of course, overall insulation is closely connected with the specific insulation, or with one or more of its components, but the influence of the surface area in Newton's equation also means that changes of posture can, by altering the effective area available for heat loss, exert an important effect. This is why animals usually curl up in a cold environment and, when possible, huddle together with others ; both responses decrease the surface area relative to volume, and in the latter situation part of the surface is exposed to the microclimate resulting from the close group association. The metabolic cost of thermoregulation is thereby reduced. Conversely, in high temperatures, animals will spread out the limbs to present the greatest possible area for loss of heat.

Activity on the part of the animal also accelerates heat loss by increasing the surface area exposed and the movement of air over the surface. This effect, however, may be offset by an increase in heat production.

2.2. CHANNELS OF HEAT EXCHANGE

The physical factors governing the exchange of heat between the body and its surroundings are basically simple and depend largely upon the temperature or vapour pressure gradients between the body surface and the environment. The relative importance of the individual channels of conduction, convection, radiation and evaporation, varies widely in different conditions and in practice special techniques are necessary to determine accurately the proportion of the total heat exchange occurring by way of each. A typical pattern in the partition of heat losses is shown in fig. 2.6.

2.2.1. Conduction

We are already familiar with the conduction of heat from the core to the surface through the body tissues. The same laws apply in the transfer of heat between the body surface and the environment. Heat is carried by conduction as the molecules of a material collide with one another ; it is transferred between two media that are in contact without any actual translocation of the molecules of either medium. The basic equation is :

$$K = \kappa A \frac{(T_{su} - T_{ob})}{d}$$

where $T_{su} - T_{ob}$ is the temperature difference between the surface of

33

the body and some external object of thickness d. In practice, the rate of heat loss from the skin of a naked animal will depend upon the thermal conductivity (k) of the material in contact with the skin. True conduction to the air will be negligible since its conductivity is so low, one-fiftieth of the value for glass, for instance. That to silver would be some four hundred times that to glass. A subjective impression

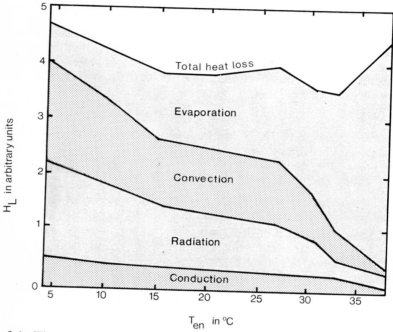

Fig. 2.6. The effect of environmental temperature on the partition of heat loss (H_L) from a pig. (Redrawn from Bond *et al.*, *Agric. Engin.*, 1952.)

of the conductivity of a material is readily gained simply by contact with a number of objects at the same temperature. Thus we are soon aware of losing a great deal more heat to a slab of marble than to a wooden table in winter, or of gaining it from a hot rock rather than a log in summer. In such a situation we can at once comprehend the significance of the area (A) of contact between the conducting surfaces and see that changes in posture may play a substantial role.

In man, conductive losses are normally small, although in exceptional cases, notably in the Australian aborigines and the Indians of Tierra del Fuego (see Chapter 7), a large part of the naked body contacts the cold ground and conductive losses are then highly significant. The very opposite situation obtains in animals with thick fur, since the area of real contact is minimal ; this is shown most dramatically by the husky dog which hardly melts the snow upon which it lies.

While the conductive transfer of heat is in most cases of minor importance in the terrestrial animals, it is the chief avenue of heat loss to water. Because of the high thermal conductivity of this medium, the loss of heat from a homoiotherm is twenty or more times as rapid as to air, as is shown by the fact that a man can survive for only a few minutes in water at 0°C, the actual period being determined to a great extent by the thickness of his insulating layer of subcutaneous fat. Those marine homoiotherms, such as whales and sea cows (Sirenia), that do not possess an effective waterproof fur, preserve their high core temperatures only by depositing a thick layer of blubber beneath the skin across which there may be a thermal difference of up to 40 K.

A small part of the body heat exchange may also occur in the conductive warming or cooling of ingested food and drink so that it is assimilated to the body temperature. Such effects, however, are generally of short duration and of relatively small significance.

2.2.2. Convection

In contrast to heat transfer by conduction, that by convection results from the movements of the molecules of the fluid in contact with the body surface. Natural convection occurs because the fluid in direct contact with the body surface is warmed, causing it to expand and decrease in density. It is then replaced by cooler fluid as it rises. Forced convection on the other hand results, not from a difference in temperature, but from an external pressure exerted on the fluid as it flows past the body. An example of this is that resulting from the passage of air in and out of the respiratory tract during breathing movements ; convective heat loss in man due to warming the inspired air accounts under comfortable conditions (20°C) for about 3 per cent of the total. We also make use of forced convection when we use a fan.

For an inanimate object or for a motionless animal body, the rate of convective heat loss (C) is given by :

$$C = h_c A \sqrt{v} (T_{su} - T_{en})$$

in which h_c is the convective coefficient, depending on the dimensions of the body and its orientation in the fluid flow ; v is the velocity of fluid movement. The direct measurement of convective exchange is more difficult if an animal moves or changes its shape, because such activities cause complicating factors by turbulence.

We see that the rate of convective heat loss would be proportional to the square root of the velocity of air movement. In practice, low wind speeds are relatively more effective in this respect than high speeds, probably because it is at the low velocities that the insulating layer of still air next to the skin is first disrupted. When this has once happened a further increase does accelerate heat loss further, although at a declining rate. As we saw in connexion with insulation, the success of fur, feathers or clothing in resisting the influence of wind rests upon its ability to maintain the integrity of the 'private climate' of still air next to the body surface.

Convective currents of air not only carry heat away directly but also increase the loss by evaporation. Because of this effect the net transfer of heat may still be in the direction of loss from the body even when the environmental temperature is above that of the body surface and heat is actually being gained by convection itself.

2.2.3. *Radiation*

In radiant heat exchange the energy travels by electromagnetic waves at the speed of light. Any object at a temperature above absolute zero radiates power in accordance with the Stefan–Boltzmann law :

$$R = \epsilon \sigma A T^4.$$

For a perfectly 'black body' $R = \sigma A T^4$; ϵ is the emissivity of the object, this being the fraction of the radiation of a perfectly black body at the same temperature that it emits ; σ is the Stefan–Boltzmann constant $(5 \cdot 67 \times 10^{-8} \text{ W m}^{-2} \text{ K}^{-4})$, A is the effective radiating area, and T is the surface temperature in kelvin.

An animal, however, not only emits long-wavelength radiant energy but also receives it from objects in the environment, as well as short-wavelength energy from the sun. The consequent net transfer is given by J. D. Hardy's formula :

$$R = \epsilon_{su} \epsilon_{en} \sigma A (T_{su}^4 - T_{en}^4)$$

in which ϵ_{su} and ϵ_{en} are the emissivities of the body surface and of the environment, and T_{su} and T_{en} are the respective temperatures in kelvin.

The property of emissivity (or 'blackness') is important physiologically because radiant energy which is reflected and not absorbed cannot contribute to the internal heat load of an animal. A perfect black body absorbs all of the radiation it receives and reflects none ; its emissivity, is (by definition) unity. Soot approaches this value $(0 \cdot 93)$ whereas highly polished silver, with an emissivity of $0 \cdot 02$, is a very good approximation to a perfect reflector. Emissivity varies with the wavelength of the radiation. Human skin, for example, irrespective of its colour, behaves as an almost perfect black body in the infra-red region, although 30–40 per cent of the energy of visible light is reflected by white skin but only about 18 per cent by black.

The proportion of the total heat loss from the body which occurs by radiation depends not only on the temperature difference between the

36

surface and the environment, but also on the effective radiating area. Areas of the surface which radiate merely to other surfaces, as between the fingers or under the arms, do not contribute to overall heat loss. In the normal extended position, about 75 per cent of the total body surface in man is available for effective radiation, and under average comfortable conditions at least 60 per cent of the overall heat loss occurs by this route.

2.2.4. *Evaporation*

The continual loss of mass of the body which occurs between meals has been known for centuries to be largely the result of water evaporated from the skin and respiratory tract. The loss of heat which accompanies the evaporation is termed insensible, to distinguish it from the sensible or direct heat that is lost by the other three channels and which occurs only in the presence of appropriate thermal gradients. In conditions which eliminate the normal gradients from the body surface to the environment, sensible heat loss is no longer possible and the maintenance of homoiothermy then depends entirely on the animal's ability to evaporate water.

By the ' vapour pressure ' at any period we mean the partial pressure of water vapour in the air. Dalton's law of partial pressures explains why the water vapour behaves just as if the air were not there at all, from the point of view of travelling about. A *vapour pressure* gradient thus propels water vapour along like a pressure gradient.

The rate of evaporation depends on the vapour pressure gradient that exists between the animal and its environment and on the resistance to the movement of vapour down the gradient.

The water vapour pressure at any point in the environmental air is determined by the mass of water vapour per unit volume around that point ; the animal can evaporate water into an atmosphere already saturated with water vapour provided that the air temperature is below that of the evaporating surface.

The reason for this is that water molecules both enter and leave the skin at rates that depend (*a*) on the partial pressures and (*b*) on the temperatures. If the partial pressures are equal for both skin and air at 100 per cent saturation the net direction of movement will be towards the lower temperature. When air temperature equals skin temperature there is dynamic equilibrium, and loss by evaporation ceases. This is presumably what happened in the infamous Black Hole of Calcutta, for in the poorly ventilated prison cell, air temperature must quickly have risen to skin temperature while complete saturation resulted from the prisoners' breath and sweat. In these conditions, body temperature would rise and heat-death become inevitable.

The actual loss of heat during evaporation depends on the change of state of the water from the aqueous to the gaseous phase, a process which absorbs heat from the surroundings. The precise value of the specific latent heat of vaporization varies with temperature, and that most widely used in physiology is $2\cdot45$ kJ g^{-1} ($2\cdot5$ MJ kg^{-1}), which is the value for water at 30°C.

The physiological efficiency of evaporation depends to a large degree on the site from which it occurs. If it is from the skin or the respiratory tract the majority of the heat will be derived from the body itself, but if it occurs from the surface of the fur or clothing most of the heat will be taken up from the air with very little cooling effect on the body.

The overall rate of evaporative heat loss (E) may be given by the equation :

$$E = E_{sk} + E_{re}$$

in which E_{sk} represents heat loss by vaporization from the skin and E_{re} that lost from the respiratory tract. Most simply, the value of E would be derived as the product of the mass of water evaporated (equivalent to the loss of body-weight, Δm) and the specific latent heat of vaporization (l) :

$$E = \Delta m l.$$

The value of the separate components from the skin and respiratory tract could be calculated as follows :

$$E_{sk} = h_e(P_{sk} - P_{en})A_W A$$

where A is the area of the evaporating surface and A_W the fraction of this surface that is actually wet ; P_{sk} is the vapour pressure of the skin and P_{en} that of the environmental air. The factor h_e is the evaporation coefficient which incorporates both a vaporization constant and environmental factors such as air velocity and direction.

Heat lost by respiratory evaporation is accelerated, not by the secretion of sweat and the consequent increase in the wetted area, but by enhancing the ventilation of the evaporating surfaces :

$$E_{re} = A \dot{V}(P_{re} - P_{en})$$

in which $\dot{V}$ is the rate of respiratory ventilation. (P_{re} here will be the vapour pressure at the surface of the upper respiratory tract, which, at least during conditions of heat stress, will be at approximately the temperature of the body core.)

If we are to be precise, the amount of heat involved in the transformation of water into vapour incorporates not only the specific latent heat of vaporization at the temperature of the evaporating surface, but also the subsequent cooling of the vapour to atmospheric temperature and its isothermal expansion to the relative humidity of the atmosphere. The cooling effect of the last two stages is probably negligible in the case of respiratory evaporation, because they would occur at some distance from the respiratory tract, but in a naked, sweating animal like man, they take place within a few millimetres of the skin surface. An example will illustrate their importance. The specific latent heat alone at a skin temperature of 33°C is about 2·42 MJ kg^{-1} ; if the vapour is cooled to 100 per cent saturation at an environmental temperature of, say, 27°C, this requires a further 0·038 kJ ; expansion from 100 per cent saturation to, say, 20 per cent then requires another 0·22 kJ. The total heat absorbed under these conditions therefore turns out to be 2·68 MJ kg^{-1}, an increase of nearly 11 per cent.

CHAPTER 3
physiological regulation of heat production

OUR primary concern in this book is with the physiology of animals at the whole-organism level. We are therefore rather more interested in the intensity of the overall process of metabolism or heat production than in the details of the numerous cellular processes that make it up. If we investigate how metabolic rate varies with body size, as well as how it varies with environmental conditions, we should be able to make predictions about how the total demands of the animal can be expected to relate to the total energy resources of its surroundings, and thus hope eventually to come to a better understanding of the immensely complex subject of animal energetics.

The ultimate source of all energy on earth is radiation from the sun, and animals are dependent upon transformation of this into a chemical form by means of photosynthesis by plants. Directly or indirectly, the chemical energy then forms the basis of animal metabolism.

3.1. *METABOLIC ACTIVITY*

3.1.1. *Basal and Standard Metabolism*

The rate of metabolic activity exhibited by an animal varies widely according to a whole range of bodily and environmental conditions. Because comparative physiology rests on the assumption that animals of different types have sufficient in common to make comparison worthwhile, when we measure metabolism we try to eliminate as many of these variable conditions as possible, so that any discrepancies that do exist reflect genuine differences of function rather than arbitrary

Organ	Per cent heat production	Rate of heat production in W	Per cent of total mass
Muscle	20	16·8 ⎫	
Skin	5	4·1 ⎬	52
Liver	20	16·8 ⎫	
Kidney	7	5·8 ⎬	6
Heart	11	9·2 ⎭	
Brain	18	15·0	2
Other	19	15·6	40

Table 1. Rate of heat production of various organs at rest in a 63 kg man. Data from Carlson and Hsieh in Edholm and Bacharach, *Physiology of Human Survival*, 1965.

factors in the environment. Metabolic rate is influenced by a host of factors, among which the most obvious include ambient temperature, digestion of food, muscular activity and time of day, although there is an almost infinite list of others as well.

To measure what is called basal metabolic rate (BMR) in a homoiotherm we try to ensure that the animal is at complete physical rest, is in a post-absorptive condition (i.e. has not taken food for at least 12 hours) and is exposed to a temperature within its thermoneutral zone. Thus the basal metabolic rate is in many ways an artificial value, but it is the best approximation attainable of the minimum energy expenditure of the organism necessary to maintain its steady state. In the average man weighing 65 kg, the overall basal rate of heat production is at about 85 W, the various organs contributing roughly as shown in table 1.

As we saw in Chapter 1, the metabolism of a poikilotherm varies with ambient temperature in much the same way as a chemical reaction. For these animals there can therefore be no zone of thermoneutrality in which to make measurements, but instead a standard metabolic rate (SMR) is estimated under conditions similar to those for homoiotherms and at some specified and biologically significant temperature. Ideally, the standard metabolic rate might be measured under several thermal conditions and the results expressed as a function of temperature.

The most satisfactory comparison between the basal metabolism or standard metabolism of different species is made using animals of the same body mass, because, as we shall see shortly, this property has a profound influence on heat production in all living things. In order to compare the heat production of homoiotherms with that of poikilotherms it is desirable to use animals, not only of similar size but also at similar body temperature. We can do this either by warming the poikilotherm to the normal body temperature of the homoiotherm—if it

Animal	Mass in kg	Surface area in m^2	Heat production in W kg^{-1}	in W m^{-2}
Elephant (young)	1360·0	13·7	0·57	56·7
Sturgeon	1400·0	11·8	0·01	1·5
Chicken	1·1	0·11	4·41	42·1
Lizard	1·2	0·11	0·12	1·4
Pigeon	0·28	0·04	4·87	32·4
Fish	0·25	—	—	1·6
Rat	0·15	0·026	7·77	45·9
Turtle	0·14	0·02	0·56	3·1
Mouse	0·06	0·01	6·26	26·6
Frog	0·05	—	—	6·3

Table 2. Heat production under basal or standard conditions in various homoiotherms and poikilotherms arranged in pairs on the basis of size. Data from Spector, *Handbook of Biological Data*, 1956.

can survive such treatment without distress—or by cooling the homoiotherm in ice while preventing with drugs any resultant increase in heat
production due to shivering. The latter procedure suffers from being
entirely artificial, and in practice, where the poikilotherm is incapable of
tolerating a body temperature of 37–40°C, measurements of its metabolic
rate are made at a series of lower temperatures, the Q_{10} value computed
from the measurements, and the metabolism at the higher temperature
estimated by extrapolation. Whichever of these methods is employed,
comparison between homoiotherms and poikilotherms of equal size
always reveals that the former produce heat at many times the rate of
the latter (table 2).

3.1.2. *The Curve of Heat Production*

In fig. 1.8 we depicted the relationship between heat production and
environmental temperature in a hypothetical homoiotherm. Having
now, in Chapter 2, also become acquainted with the physical and some
of the physiological conditions which combine to produce the ' curve
of heat production ', we are in a position to examine the relationship in

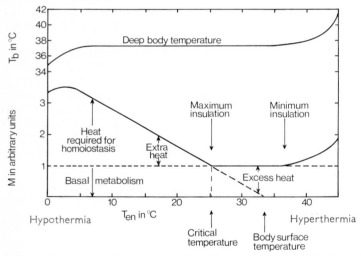

Fig. 3.1. The curve of heat production. For comparison with fig. 1.8.

more detail (fig. 3.1). Accordingly, throughout the remainder of this
chapter we shall be concerned chiefly with the birds and mammals
since they are the only animals which have evolved, as one of the central
elements of their thermoregulatory system, a high rate of endothermic
heat production which is regulated independently of ambient temperature.

42

We know from our adaptation of Newton's law that if the rate of heat production in a given individual is equal to the rate of heat loss from the body surface, then it is also proportional to the thermal gradient between the surface and the environment. When this gradient is eliminated, that is when the surface temperature and environmental temperature are equal, the rate of cooling by direct transfer would be zero. However, since there can never be zero heat production during the life of an animal, the corresponding extrapolation of the heat production line in fig. 3.1 to the horizontal axis is of theoretical interest only. In practice, the basal metabolic rate is reached at the critical temperature of the environment, and between this and the upper critical temperature metabolism remains constant and heat is lost mainly by the vaporization of water. Within the thermoneutral zone the constancy of metabolism implies that the insulation of the body shell must decrease in proportion to the rising temperature in order to maintain homoiothermy. This is achieved very largely by increasing the quantity of blood flowing to the skin. The excess heat, that is the quantity produced over and above that theoretically necessary to maintain body temperature, increases as the environmental temperature rises above the critical level. It has to be dissipated by the physical regulatory mechanisms, and if these become inadequate, there is a rise in body temperature and ultimately death in hyperthermia.

Below the critical temperature heat production rises as the surroundings become cooler. The maximum level of insulation has by now been achieved and homoiothermy is maintained only at the expense of a

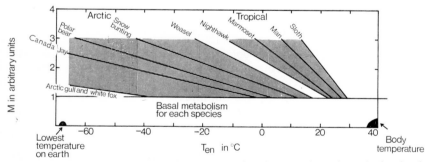

Fig. 3.2. The effect on the metabolic rate of various arctic and tropical animals of exposure to low environmental temperatures. The curves show the critical temperatures, where metabolism rises above the basal level (shown as one unit) and the rates of extra heat production for each species. Tropical animals are poorly insulated and therefore have critical temperatures close to body temperature and steep curves of metabolism. Arctic animals are well insulated, have low critical temperatures and, in the case of the gull and fox, can tolerate the coldest temperature on earth merely by raising metabolism by 30–40 per cent. (Based on work by Scholander *et al.*, *Biol. Bull.*, 1950.)

43

raised metabolism. The extra heat, namely that produced by chemical regulation, increases as the gradient between the critical temperature and the actual ambient temperature widens (fig. 3.1) ; ultimately, the heat required to maintain homoiostasis exceeds that which may be released from the metabolic reserves of the individual, there is a fall in body temperature, and death in hypothermia.

The slope of the line relating heat production to falling ambient temperature varies inversely with the overall efficiency of the insulation. Similarly, the actual value of the critical temperature in a given species is a function of this insulation. These points have been elegantly demonstrated in an interspecific study by P. F. Scholander and others, a summary of which is presented in fig. 3.2.

3.1.3. *Measurement of Metabolism*

Many of the techniques of modern physiology are so complicated that nothing short of a specialized course of instruction is adequate to master them. Yet a proper understanding of the principles upon which a method is based is essential if any data obtained by its use are fully to be appreciated, both for their value and for their limitations, and if any interpretations thus derived are to be theoretically sound. In the case of metabolism it is a relief to discover that measurements are relatively easy to make ; even the most sophisticated apparatus can be understood in terms of simple physical and chemical principles and we need not describe the methods in great detail in order to have an adequate comprehension of how the results are obtained.

3.1.3.1. *Direct methods*

The first measurements of metabolism in animals were made by Adair Crawford (1748–95) in Scotland in 1777, and involved estimations of the heat given off in terms of the increase in temperature of a known amount of water in a chamber surrounding the animal. Since the loss of heat from the calorimeter was minimized by insulation the cause of the rise in temperature must have been heat from the animal. This is why the method is called direct.

Only two years later the Frenchmen Antoine Lavoisier (1743–94) and Pierre Laplace (1749–1827) successfully determined the relationship between the heat lost from a homoiotherm and that entering it in the form of food. This was a major step forward. First, they constructed a calorimeter similar to Crawford's except that its action depended upon collecting the quantity of water melted by the animal from ice (fig. 3.3) ; then they measured the amount of carbon dioxide produced by the animal in the same time, and calculated the quantity of ice that would be melted if carbon were burnt to form the same amount of gas. In obtaining close agreement between the two approaches they established

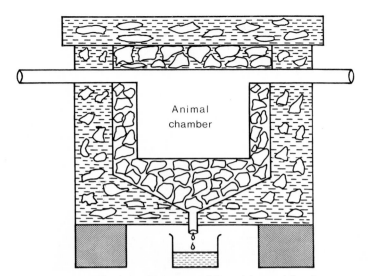

Fig. 3.3. The ice-calorimeter of Lavoisier and Laplace.

the basis for animal calorimetry in terms of oxygen consumption and chemical combustion (which led to the collapse of the old phlogiston theory), and with it the whole foundation of future work in metabolism

Nowadays there are two basic types of direct calorimeter in use The first is in essentials a descendant of Crawford's original 'heat-sink' type of instrument, in which heat is prevented from entering or leaving the calorimeter by means of an insulating jacket and that produced by the animal is removed by circulating water. The exchange of heat due to the animal is then measured as the product of the rate of flow of the water and the difference in its temperature on entry and exit from the apparatus.

The second or 'thermal gradient' type of calorimeter is more than a hundred years later in conception. Instead of preventing the flow of heat through the walls of the instrument, the rate of this flow is measured across concentrically arranged spaces around the animal. Calibration is performed by first using a heat source of known output inside the chamber. A modern version employing this principle is the gradient-layer calorimeter. A thin layer of material of uniform thermal conductivity surrounds the animal in an 'integrating sphere' (which may be of any shape) and the temperature difference across it is detected by numerous thermo-junctions. The total rate of heat loss by the animal is then computed by integrating all the individual measurements, a useful procedure because it permits rapid changes to be followed (fig. 3.4).

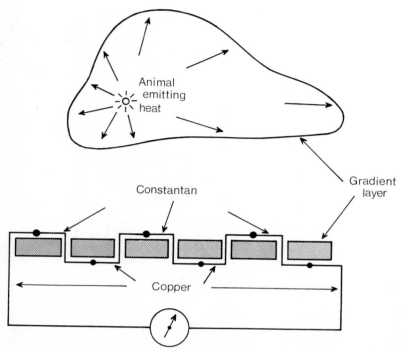

Fig. 3.4. The principle of the gradient-layer calorimeter. The gradient layer consists of copper-constantan junctions woven through an insulating layer. If it lines the surface of the animal chamber uniformly and completely it records the total heat emitted from within the chamber regardless of the position of the animal or the size and shape of the chamber. (Redrawn from *The Energy Metabolism of Ruminants*, by K. L. Blaxter, Hutchinson, 1962.)

3.1.3.2. *Indirect methods*

One of the results of Lavoisier's original demonstration of the close similarity between the heat generated by an animal and the energy content of its food was the development of one of the two main types of indirect calorimetry, that depending on studies of total energy balance. In this method the energy input is assumed to be equal to that of the food minus that of the excreta ; the difference allows us to make an estimate of the energy used by the animal in unit time. In these experiments the calorific content of the food and faeces are determined from the rise in temperature of a known quantity of water caused by burning weighed samples in oxygen in what is known as a bomb calorimeter (fig. 3.5).

Perhaps the most widely used indirect method of measuring metabolism is that of respiration calorimetry. Although there are many

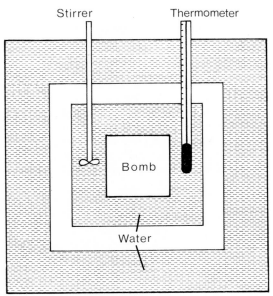

Fig. 3.5. The principle of the bomb calorimeter. A weighed sample of the food or faeces is burned in high-pressure oxygen inside the bomb. The heat of combustion is calculated from the specific heat capacity of the bomb and water, and the rise in temperature of the water.

different techniques, each with its own advantages and disadvantages, they fall naturally into two groups, the closed-circuit and open-circuit systems.

Once again we owe to Lavoisier the conception that has led in subsequent years to the development of a whole range of closed-circuit methods. You will recall that Lavoisier needed to measure the carbon dioxide production of his animals in order to make comparisons with results obtained using the direct ice-calorimeter. His own method for this was simply to enclose a guinea pig in a bell jar set in a trough of mercury, and to estimate its carbon dioxide output by the fall in volume of the combined gases in the jar after the introduction of a piece of sodium hydroxide. From the difference between the initial and final volumes of the gases he was also able to measure the oxygen consumed.

The apparatus developed by Henri Regnault (1810–78) and Jules Reiset (1818–96) in the middle of the nineteenth century represents a marked improvement over the original closed-circuit system, in that the animal does not suffer from a progressive accumulation of carbon dioxide throughout the experiment. In modern versions the air is circulated through a carbon dioxide absorber and the oxygen consumed by the animal is continually replaced from a cylinder so that there is no

47

change in pressure. The quantity of oxygen thus introduced is a measure of the consumption by the animal (fig. 3.6).

One of the principal sources of error in the Regnault–Reiset apparatus lies in the fact that the volume of air is large compared to the animal ; because small differences have to be measured between two large volumes, a small percentage error in the latter yields a large one in the final result. This is overcome by the use of a spirometric method (fig. 3.7). The respiratory tract of the animal or subject is connected by a cannula in the trachea or by some form of mask to a bell (the spirometer) containing oxygen. The breathing movements cause the bell to fluctuate up and down and it gradually descends as the oxygen is used up and the expired carbon dioxide is absorbed by a canister of soda lime. The

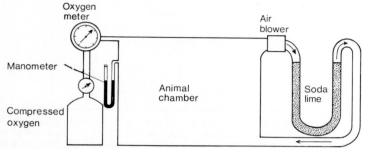

Fig. 3.6. A simple closed-circuit respiration calorimeter.

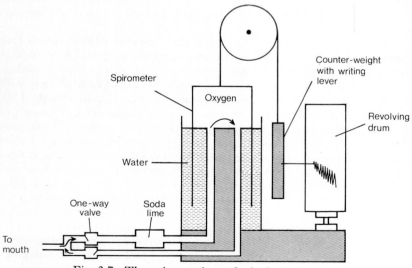

Fig. 3.7. The spirometric method of calorimetry.

change in volume is recorded by a lever which writes on a revolving drum so that at the termination of the experiment the slope of the line gives a measure of the oxygen consumption per unit time.

Instead of using changes in pressure or volume to calculate metabolic rate in terms of oxygen consumed, closed-circuit respiration calorimetry can also be used in conjunction with gas analysis (see below). All that is necessary is to measure the oxygen concentration in a sample of the air breathed at the start and end of the experiment, together with the total volume of air in the closed space. Such a crude method is, however, seldom used in practice.

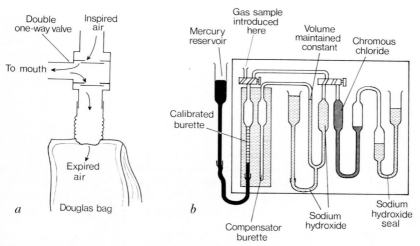

Fig. 3.8. A simple open-circuit method of respiration calorimetry used in conjunction with the Haldane gas analysis apparatus. See text.

Of the open-circuit methods of respiration calorimetry the simplest is that using a one-way valve and a gas-collecting bag (fig. 3.8 a). Air is breathed in from the outside atmosphere but the expired air is collected in a flexible (Douglas) bag which is later emptied through a gas meter to determine the expired volume. Small samples of the air are analysed for oxygen and carbon dioxide and from these measurements the metabolism can be calculated. Accurate gas analysis is essential for this and similar techniques. The traditional method has been a chemical one and its most popular representative is the apparatus devised by John Scott Haldane (1860–1936) (fig. 3.8 b). Use of this is very much a practical exercise. Briefly, a sample of inspired or expired air is introduced into the calibrated burette, where its volume is measured at atmospheric pressure. The air is then brought into contact with the carbon dioxide absorber (sodium hydroxide) and the reduction in volume noted. The oxygen present is next absorbed by a strong reducing agent such as chromous chloride and the residual gas considered to be nitrogen. The compensator burette eliminates errors due to changes in temperature or pressure during analysis if all readings are taken with the burette connected to the sodium hydroxide and with its volume constant. There are many other, more modern methods, which it is not necessary for us to examine ; they mostly depend upon measurements of various physical properties of gases, although initial calibration is always from known gas mixtures or by one of the established chemical-volumetric techniques like that outlined above.

Finally, one recently developed method of indirect calorimetry that is worth mentioning is that which employs doubly labelled isotopic water $D_2^{18}O$ (each of the components of water is labelled with a stable isotope, deuterium for hydrogen and oxygen-18 for oxygen). Briefly, the principle underlying this method is that the turnover of the hydrogen in body water is slower than that of oxygen, because it is lost to the environment only in water, whereas oxygen passes out both in water and carbon dioxide. The degree of this difference is proportional to the rate of carbon dioxide output, which can be estimated indirectly as an indicator of metabolism simply by analysing blood samples taken immediately after injection of the labelled water, and again, after a suitable lapse of time, for changes in the specific activity of the isotopes. To do this an instrument called a mass spectrometer is required. Given the appropriate facilities, this method of measuring metabolism overcomes one of the chief drawbacks of all the others, namely, the artificial confinement to which the animal is subjected.

3.1.4. *The Respiratory Quotient*

In practice the measurement of metabolism by respiratory methods often relies solely on estimates of oxygen consumption, and as a consequence the results can be expressed only as oxygen uptake per unit time. If we wish to compare results obtained by different (direct and indirect) calorimetric methods we need, in addition, information on the carbon dioxide output over the same period. Failing this information, we can derive only a rough approximation to heat production by making an assumption about the heat equivalent of the food being oxidized. In clinical work this is often done because so much work has been performed on man utilizing a normal diet that we know quite closely how much energy is made available for each litre of oxygen used up.

For more accurate work we measure both carbon dioxide production and oxygen consumption and express the two as a ratio :

$$\frac{\text{Volume of carbon dioxide produced in unit time}}{\text{Volume of oxygen consumed in the same time}}$$

$$= \text{Respiratory quotient (RQ)}.$$

50

Once the value of the respiratory quotient is known, the relative proportions of fat and carbohydrate being oxidized can readily be estimated because we know how much heat is given off during the oxidation of either pure fat or pure carbohydrate alone. These, at standard temperature and pressure, are 19·7 kJ l^{-1} O_2 and 20·9 kJ l^{-1} O_2 respectively. For protein the corresponding figure is 18·4 kJ. In many experiments the protein is ignored since it is not oxidized in significant quantities by normal fasting animals (other than carnivores).

In the case where only carbohydrate is being oxidized, the respiratory quotient will be equal to one, because hydrogen and oxygen are present in the carbohydrate molecule in the proportions that form water :

$$C_x(H_2O)_y + xO_2 \rightarrow xCO_2 + yH_2O.$$

With other foodstuffs, however, there is relatively less oxygen and the respiratory quotient is therefore lower. In the case of fat, for example, it is about 0·7. Once the respiratory quotient has been calculated from the volume measurements the calorific equivalents appropriate to the experiment are read off from one of the many available tables of metabolic constants.

Where a really high degree of accuracy is essential we must also take into account the protein oxidation. There is no representative value for the respiratory quotient for protein because it depends on the type of aminoacids being oxidized, but an average value of about 0·8 is generally accepted. In the metabolism of protein, oxidation is incomplete and organic nitrogen compounds are excreted by the animal (mostly as urea in mammals and as uric acid in birds). Since protein contains about 16 per cent nitrogen, the excreta can be used to estimate the amount of protein oxidized, as well as the quantities of oxygen consumed and carbon dioxide produced in the process. These values are then subtracted from the total gas volumes and the non-protein respiratory quotient is calculated. From this, in turn, an accurate estimate can be made of the relative proportions of fat and carbohydrate being metabolized. When the quantities of the three foodstuffs being oxidized are known, they are multiplied by the appropriate calorific equivalents and the total heat produced is calculated. The figure obtained gives the amount of heat that ought to be liberated from the chemical energy made available ; when compared with direct measurements of the actual

	0·7	0·8	0·9	1·0
Non-protein respiratory quotient	0·7	0·8	0·9	1·0
Heat production (kJ l^{-1} O_2 consumed)	19·7	20·1	20·5	20·9
Heat production (kJ l^{-1} CO_2 released)	28·1	25·1	23·0	20·9
Percentage O_2 consumed by carbohydrate	0	32	66	100
Percentage O_2 consumed by fat	100	68	34	0
Quantity of carbohydrate consumed (g) l^{-1} O_2	0·0	0·4	0·8	1·2
Quantity of fat consumed (g) l^{-1} O_2	0·5	0·4	0·2	0·0

Table 3. Some useful metabolic constants.

51

heat liberated during the same period, the two results seldom differ by more than 1 per cent. Indeed, it is from such experiments that the standard tables given in most textbooks are derived (table 3).

It is important to realize that the respiratory quotient can only be a crude indication of the role being played by the various pathways of cellular metabolism. Thus while remembering its great value in normal circumstances, we should not forget that it may be affected by factors other than just the composition of the diet. Among these are exercise, acid-base disturbances such as those associated with starvation or over-breathing, and metabolic interconversions such as the transformation of protein into carbohydrate or of carbohydrate into fat.

3.1.5. *Heat Production at the Cellular Level*

From our equation above depicting the oxidation of carbohydrate, we omitted the energy released during the burning. It is from the oxidation of glucose that the cell obtains the energy for the rest of its activities, thus :

$$C_6H_{12}O_6 + 6O_2 \rightarrow 6CO_2 + 6H_2O + 2818 \text{ kJ}.$$

That is, the burning of one mole of glucose (which is 180 g) yields about 2818 kJ of energy in the form of heat. The cell does not perform this extraordinary feat in one step, but through a series of nearly thirty stages, each reaction providing a small and economic packet of energy which can be conserved by the body or used to build the fuel which it needs in performing its various kinds of work. Nevertheless, the same quantity of heat is released no matter whether it is by this gradual series of enzyme-controlled reactions or by direct burning of the glucose to carbon dioxide.

To return for a moment to more general ground, it is worthwhile recalling the distinction between the various biochemical processes, the total sum of which we refer to as metabolism. Processes which break down complex molecules into simple ones are called catabolic and these, generally speaking, are energy-yielding reactions (called exergonic or, more loosely, exothermic) that can proceed spontaneously without the need for an external source of energy. Processes which synthesize complex molecules are called anabolic and these involve an increase in free energy and therefore proceed only with an external source of supply (endergonic, or endothermic). We are concerned here only with reactions of the first kind, since much of the energy which they make available is degraded into heat and used to keep the body warm. Because the body temperature of a homoiotherm is normally above that of the environment, and heat is therefore lost down the thermal gradient, its continual generation is essential. The maintenance of the gradient despite the continual loss of heat is what indicates to us that exergonic energy transformations, or basal metabolic activities, are going on in the organism.

As has already been said, we cannot here concern ourselves with the full details of the intermediary metabolic pathways which provide heat for the body from the breakdown of food. Nevertheless, it is as well to summarize briefly the outlines of these energy-yielding reactions, so that we may keep in mind the vital importance of the fundamental processes which underlie our own particular use of the word metabolism. The details form a well-known story which you can find in any textbook of biochemistry.

Carbohydrates like glucose are not the only foodstuffs utilized by the body in the first steps towards the breakdown into simple molecules ; fats and protein are also involved. The whole complex process is perhaps best understood in terms of the three phases described by H. A. Krebs and H. L. Kornberg (fig. 3.9). In the first phase, the three basic and complex foods are broken down during digestion into their simple component parts. The carbohydrates are converted into monosaccharide sugars by the action of enzymes such as amylase in the saliva and panreatic juice. The fats are broken down into glycerol and fatty acids largely by the lipases of the small intestine. Finally, the proteins

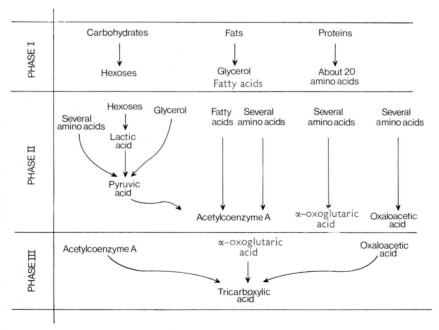

Fig. 3.9. The three phases of the production of energy from food. (Based on Krebs and Kornberg, *Physiol. Biol. Chem. Expl Pharm.*, 1957.)

53

become transformed into about twenty different aminoacids by the gastric pepsin and intestinal trypsin. These relatively small molecules pass through the intestinal wall to enter the blood stream either directly, or indirectly via the lymphatic system, and it is by this means that the cells themselves (or rather the mitochondria) are kept well supplied with a source of food in a form that they can use.

The production of these substances of low molecular weight is accompanied by the release of a negligible amount of free energy. The sugars, fatty acids and aminoacids are then broken down, in phase two, through a series of reactions, once again with the release of little energy, to the three simple acids, pyruvic (combined in the cell with coenzyme A to give acetylcoenzyme A), oxaloacetic and α-oxoglutaric. The acetylcoenzyme A and the two types of aminoacid residue, being metabolically quite similar, now come together and enter a common

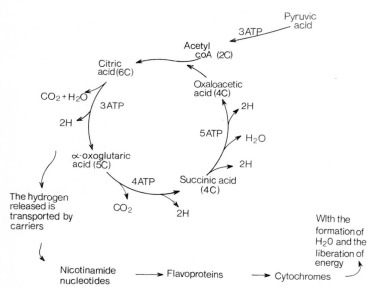

Fig. 3.10. A simplified outline of the tricarboxylic acid cycle showing how 15 molecules of adenosine triphosphate (ATP) are produced in stages from the breakdown of each molecule of pyruvic acid. The 2-carbon (2C) fragment of acetylcoenzyme A combines with the 4-carbon oxaloacetic acid to give 6-carbon citric acid. This is broken down to 5-carbon α-ketoglutaric acid with the release of one molecule of CO_2. Further breakdown to 4-carbon succinic acid follows similarly and this is finally converted back to oxaloacetic acid so that the cycle can restart. The hydrogen liberated during the cycle is transported by a series of carriers which convert it to water with the release of energy. This is used to build ATP.

54

sequence of enzyme reactions which constitute phase three, and by which all three substances are converted to carbon dioxide and water.

This series of reactions is known variously as the tricarboxylic acid- or citric-acid cycle, or as the Krebs cycle after its discoverer in the 1930s. The chemical events are linked together in such a way that the product of the first reaction represents the substrate of the second, and so on (fig. 3.10). Each step in the cycle requires a specific enzyme to catalyse it, and at certain of these steps an enormous amount of energy is released. Very simply, these energy-giving steps are the ones involving the oxidation of substrate by the transference of electrons, accompanied by hydrogen, to substances known as hydrogen-carriers. The chief of these are, in sequence, nicotinamide adenine dinucleotide (NAD), the flavoproteins and, ultimately, one of the iron-containing proteins called cytochromes. All of these accept hydrogen atoms by reduction and on oxidation yield them up again to the carrier that follows ; the final step forms water but all stages release energy. The latter is used in the synthesis of high-energy phosphate (adenosine triphosphate, ATP) which represents the universal energy-bank of the cell in that it is the source for most endergonic reactions.

The importance of this energy store is shown by the fact that hydrolysis of one mole of adenosine triphosphate to adenosine diphosphate (ADP) and inorganic phosphate, releases about 36 kJ of free energy. Conversely, during the oxidation reactions of the tricarboxylic acid cycle each step yielding 36 kJ of energy is used to build a mole of adenosine triphosphate. The energy-rich phosphate bonds therefore represent the central reserve of energy within the cell ; it is this system which allows the release of energy at a rate that the cell can cope with.

If we follow our earlier story of glucose breakdown a little further we have a good specific example of the value of each of the three phases in the release of energy. The digestive part of the process, phase one of fig. 3.9, releases no significant energy, but the second phase, that of anaerobic glycolysis, ends in the production of two molecules of adenosine triphosphate from a single molecule of glucose. However, two molecules of nicotinamide adenine dinucleotide are reduced in the process (NADH) and these are oxidized back by way of the flavoprotein–cytochrome system with the generation of a further six molecules of adenosine triphosphate. Thus, the steps up to this stage yield a combined total of eight molecules of adenosine triphosphate.

The next stage involves the conversion of pyruvic acid to acetyl-coenzyme A and the latter enters the tricarboxylic acid cycle (phase three), where the remaining carbon atoms are oxidized to carbon dioxide and water (oxidative phosphorylation) with the release of no fewer than 30 molecules of adenosine triphosphate (that is, 15 for each of the molecules of pyruvic acid). This phase in the degradation of glucose is

55

therefore overwhelmingly the most productive ; of the 38 molecules of adenosine triphosphate produced in all by complete oxidation of one molecule of glucose, only two are yielded by anaerobic glycolysis. Since the hydrolysis of one mole of adenosine triphosphate to adenosine diphosphate releases about 36 kJ, the 38 moles yield a total of some 1268 kJ. The complete burning of one mole of glucose, as we have seen, releases about 2818 kJ, so that the cell is capable of trapping in useful form almost half of the total energy released in the full oxidation of its fuel. This estimate of efficiency is, however, misleadingly high ; one of greater biological significance would have to make allowance for the energy cost of bringing the fuel to the cell in manageable form, and of carrying away energy to the site of its use. Nevertheless, the cell does compare favourably in efficiency with a modern power station, and its ability to synthesize large molecules far outstrips the performance of the most modern chemical techniques. The greater part of the energy generated is not used in anabolic activities, however, nor in the contraction of muscle or the active transport of substances across cell membranes ; at least 80 per cent of it is converted to heat for the maintenance of body temperature.

3.1.6. *Metabolism, Body Size and the Surface Area Law*

More than a century ago sufficient was already known about the relationship between the surface area and the rate of heat loss from homoiothermic animals to allow the prediction that small animals must have relatively higher rates of heat production than large ones. This is simply the result of the physical dimensions of bodies. The surface area of a spherical body is given by the formula $A = 4\pi r^2$ and the volume by $V = 4\pi r^3/3$, where r is the radius of the sphere. Thus the surface area increases as the square of the radius but the volume as the cube, and if we examine the relationship as a ratio, we get :

$$\frac{A}{V} = \frac{3(4\pi r^2)}{4\pi r^3} = \frac{3}{r}.$$

Therefore, the larger the sphere the greater is the volume relative to the surface area. Although the surface areas of animal bodies are obviously greater than those of spheres of corresponding volumes (a sphere is the geometrical shape with the smallest surface/volume ratio possible), they do, in fact, vary as regular functions of their linear dimensions in just the same way (fig. 3.11).

Since many physiological functions are affected by surface, a great deal of attention was devoted in the early years of mammalian energetics to the relationship between body surface area and metabolic rate. The classical examination of this relationship was carried out by Rubner in 1883, working on dogs. Using animals which varied in size from about

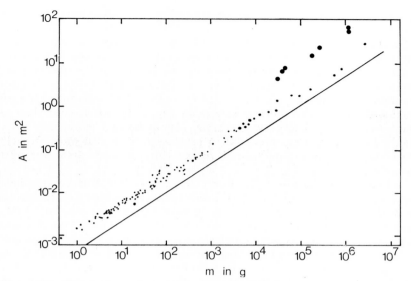

Fig. 3.11. The body surface area (A) of vertebrates in relation to mass (m). The line represents the surface area of a sphere. The large dots in the upper right-hand corner are for beech trees. (Redrawn and modified from Hemmingsen, *Rep. Steno Mem. Hosp.*, 1960.)

Number of dog	Mass in kg	Surface area in m²	Heat production in W kg⁻¹	Heat production in W m⁻²
1	31·2	1·075	1·72	50·0
2	24·0	0·881	1·97	53·7
3	19·8	0·750	2·20	58·3
4	18·2	0·766	2·23	53·0
5	9·6	0·529	3·16	57·2
6	6·5	0·372	3·19	55·7
7	3·2	0·242	4·26	58·6

Table 4. Rubner's table of heat production in dogs expressed in terms of unit mass and unit surface area.

3 to 31 kg body mass, he tabulated his results so as to emphasize the impressive decrease in metabolic rate per unit body mass which occurred as the size of the animals increased (table 4). By contrast, there was an almost constant relationship when metabolic rate was expressed in terms of unit body surface area. Thus it seemed that the heat production was indeed adjusted to the surface-related rate of heat loss. Furthermore, Rubner postulated that this relationship had a thermo-regulatory function in that the animal maintained its body warmth as a result of the stimulation of cutaneous temperature receptors by the

environment, and that they in turn controlled the metabolizing activities of the tissues.

Rubner's explanation of what soon became established as the ' surface area law ' is no longer considered valid. There are several reasons for this, among which by far the most persuasive lies in the observation, first made only a few years after the publication of Rubner's own findings but largely ignored for fifty years, that metabolic rate in poikilotherms is also more closely related to body surface area than to body weight. Poikilotherms certainly cannot be said to regulate their body warmth in proportion to their surface areas, so it is most unlikely that there could be any causal relationship between area and heat production.

There is an enormous literature on the so-called surface area law, and a great deal of effort has been spent on devising methods of measuring or calculating the surface area of bodies. Indeed, for a time, so firmly established did the ' law ' become as fundamental physiological dogma, that experimental results which appeared to contradict it were interpreted as special cases or even disregarded on the grounds of inaccurate measurement. For example, when Karl von Voit (1831–1908) published his famous table in 1901 (table 5) it was thought to

Species	Mass in kg	Heat production in W kg^{-1}	Heat production in W m^{-2}
Horse	441·0	0·54	45·8
Pig	128·0	0·93	52·1
Man	64·3	1·55	50·3
Dog	15·2	2·49	50·2
Goose	3·5	3·22	49·2
Rabbit	2·3	3·63	37·5
Domestic fowl	2·0	3·43	48·7

Table 5. Voit's table of heat production in various homoiotherms.

provide interspecific confirmation of the law that Rubner had derived using only dogs. Unfortunately, the metabolism of the rabbit fell significantly below the figure of 50 W m^{-2} which was considered characteristic of homoiotherms, but this was hastily ' corrected ' by some (though not by Voit himself) to a more acceptable figure of 44·3 W m^{-2} by using a surface area measurement that omitted the ears ! The surface area law still finds wide acceptance in the clinical literature, although in reality it has only limited value for animals in general and is at best no more than a rough, empirical approximation even for homoiotherms.

Even when it became clear that the surface area law was, in fact, a good deal less accurate and universal than had been supposed, there still remained the problem of attempting to define the exact nature of the relationship between metabolic rate and body size. Since each individual cell of an animal produces heat, it was no surprise that large animals had greater absolute rates of heat production than smaller ones. Yet it could readily be shown that the heat production per unit body mass was inversely related to some function of body size. The significance of this relationship was appreciated by M. Kleiber when he calculated that if a mouse had the same metabolic rate per unit mass as an ox, it would require fur at least 200 mm thick for adequate insulation, or conversely, that an ox with the metabolism of a mouse would need a skin temperature higher than the boiling point of water in order to lose heat at the rate at which it was produced.

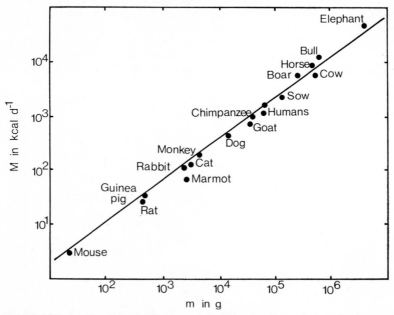

Fig. 3.12. Kleiber's original ' mouse-to-elephant ' curve relating the logarithm of metabolism to the logarithm of mass. Note that metabolism is expressed in the old units of kilocalorie per day. (Redrawn and modified from Kleiber, *Hilgardia*, 1932.)

The leading workers in this field, Kleiber himself, F. G. Benedict and S. Brody, all published important papers in the 1930s showing a strikingly linear relationship in mammals between the logarithm of metabolism and the logarithm of body mass. What is more, each of these authors also demonstrated that the relationship held over a wide range both of species and of body size. This work resulted in the drawing of the now famous ' mouse-to-elephant ' curve (fig. 3.12);

a ' hummingbird-to-ostrich ' curve can equally well be constructed and a similar relationship holds even for poikilothermic species.

Curves of this type are described by the general exponential equation : $M = am^b$, where M is metabolic rate and m is mass (body weight) ; a is the constant of proportionality and b is the exponent. In logarithmic form this gives the linear function :

$$\log M = b \log m + \log a$$

so that the value of b can be calculated from the slope of the regression line.

The value of the exponent has attracted a good deal of attention, not to say controversy. If the surface area law had been proved valid, the value of b would be $0 \cdot 67$, since surface area varies with the two-thirds power of body mass. If metabolism were proportional directly to body mass then its value would be 1. In the past, there were about as many values assigned to the exponent as investigators studying it, and much energy was wasted on arguments over the second and even third

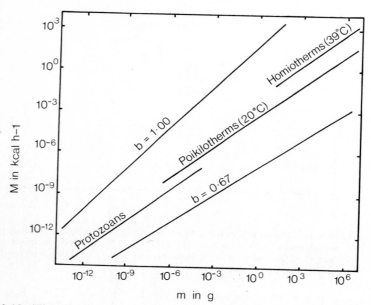

Fig. 3.13. The relation between the logarithm of metabolism and the logarithm of mass in a variety of organisms. b is the exponent in the equation $M = am^b$ and has a value of about $0 \cdot 75$ in each of the animal curves. Curves with slopes of $1 \cdot 00$ (direct proportionality) and $0 \cdot 67$ (the ' surface area law ') are shown for comparison. Note that metabolism is expressed in kilocalorie per hour. (Redrawn and modified from Hemmingsen, *Rep. Steno Mem. Hosp.*, 1960.)

decimal place. Despite this, however, almost all the computed values fell between 0·7 and 0·8, and a recent survey has shown that metabolic rate in an enormous range of organisms is most satisfactorily related to the three-fourths power of body mass (fig. 3.13), and this value was accepted in 1964 at the Energy Metabolism Symposium of the European Association for Animal Production as the reference value for all species. As is perhaps inevitable in biology, there are a few organisms, notably some molluscs and insects, which exhibit metabolism/body-mass curves of significantly different slopes, but these are so exceptional as in no way to invalidate the otherwise universal relationship. At any rate, the integrity of the value of 0·75 from unicellular organisms to the largest mammals, and even including beech trees, utterly destroys the illusion that thermoregulatory mechanisms as such are in any way involved in the relation between heat production and body size.

It may be of interest to note in passing that a statistically significant difference between values of the exponent of 0·75 (the so-called ' three-fourths power law ') and 0·67 (the ' surface area ' or ' two-thirds power law ') can be demonstrated only when animals are available which differ in size by at least 9-fold. (Each division between the coordinates in fig. 3.13 represents a difference of 1000-fold.) Thus, Rubner, in using dogs from 3 to 31 kg body weight, only just had the material to show a difference of slope from that based on surface area. If he had had available the size range of modern dogs we may like to believe that he would have spotted the difference.

3.2. *FACTORS AFFECTING METABOLISM*

3.2.1. *Thyroid Activity*

It has long been known that the increased oxygen consumption which results from exposing animals to cold is closely associated with an increase in the activity of the thyroid glands and the resultant output of thyroid hormones (TH). Also, it has now been shown that prolonged exposure to heat can lead to a depression of thyroid activity and to a small reduction in the basal metabolic rate. It is another matter, however, to explain just how the level of thyroid hormones in the blood actually regulates metabolism, and at present we are forced to admit that this occurs in a way that is still largely unknown.

Of course, we can give an outline of how, say, exposure to cold affects the nervous system and how this in turn affects the thyroid and adrenal glands. Thus, the stimulus of cold acts initially on the receptors in the skin and, if prolonged, also indirectly by way of the blood on the hypothalamus. An overall decrease in the body temperature leads at first to a tensing of the muscles and then to shivering, which greatly enhances heat production (see Section 3.23). Both the thyroid and adrenal glands probably facilitate this response in some way by their hormonal secretions.

The cold stimulus on the hypothalamus also affects the pituitary gland ; this secretes the thyroid-stimulating hormone (TSH) and the adreno-corticotropic hormone (ACTH), which act on their respective target organs to promote the secretion of thyroid hormones and the cortical steroids. The hypothalamus also elicits a response from the sympathetic nervous system by way of the adrenal medulla. The resultant secretion of adrenaline and noradrenaline accelerates glycogen breakdown and lipolysis. These effects are further promoted by interaction of the catecholamines (as adrenaline and its related compounds are called) with the thyroid hormones.

Of all these hormonal effects the influence of the thyroid hormones is probably the most important. There has been a great deal of work on the mechanism of action of thyroid hormones on mitochondrial respiration, but there is as yet no clear picture of what happens, and consequently little point in our spending time on details. Suffice it to say that, until recently, it was believed that the heat-producing effect of thyroid hormones was accomplished by their ability to uncouple oxidative phosphorylation in intact mitochondria. This, it was held, would lead to an increased rate of metabolism by the oxidation of substrate, yet without an increased synthesis of adenosine triphosphate. Unfortunately, this elegant story is now largely discounted for several reasons, chiefly that under experimental conditions unnaturally high concentrations of thyroid hormone are necessary to promote the un-coupling, and also that there are several substances which do uncouple oxidative phosphorylation and accelerate oxygen consumption just like the thyroid hormone, but which do not share its other effects. Further-more, in poikilotherms, thyroid hormone does not increase heat production at all, though it is important as a growth-promoting sub-stance. It now seems possible that the thermogenic effect of the thyroid hormones in homoiotherms may be related to their promoting influence on the synthesis of proteins. Compounds are available which will block the heat-producing effects of the hormones by preventing protein synthesis but which do not uncouple oxidative phosphorylation.

A striking example of the importance of thyroid hormones in regulat-ing metabolism is provided by the frizzle fowl. This bird is an ordinary domestic fowl except that, owing to the action of a single dominant gene, the feathers are curled and brittle and offer little protection as an insulating coat. As a result of this the heat loss from frizzle fowls is much higher than from normal ones and their critical temperature is also much higher, about 28°C instead of 15°C. At the latter temperature the frizzles have metabolic rates about twice that of the normals despite a lowering of the body temperature. The chemical regulation upon which the frizzles depend is stimulated by an abnormally high rate of thyroid activity, but so high is the utilization of the hormones by the tissues that the level in the blood is actually lower than in normal hens. There is thus a paradoxical situation of a high rate of heat production stimulated by a high secretion rate of thyroid hormones, coupled with some of the symptoms of hypothyroidism in the gland itself. Exposure of the birds to a warm environment leads, on the other hand, to symptoms of hyperthyroidism. The frizzling of the feathers is independent of thyroid function and the abnormalities in the latter are the consequence of overstimulation, which itself is secondary to the excessive heat loss due to the frizzled plumage.

A similar situation must presumably obtain in the case of the hairless Mexican dog. This rare creature is said to maintain a constant body temperature of 40°C, a claim which, if verified, would be reason enough to justify not only a detailed physiological study, but also the breed's reputation as the world's only authentic hot dog.

3.2.2. *The Role of Brown Fat*

In mammals there are two types of adipose tissue, the white and the brown. For many years the brown tissue was believed to be a stage in the development of normal white tissue, and it was known as embryonal fat. It is now thought, however, that the two are quite distinct in that the cells of the one type do not change into cells of the other. The initial misconception was understandable, because brown fat is most prominent in young animals, although it does develop in substantial proportions in the adults of some species after cold-adaptation. Indeed,

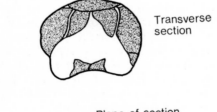

Transverse
section

Plane of section

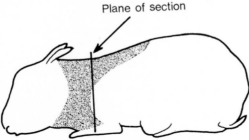

Fig. 3.14. The site and extent of brown adipose tissue in a new-born rabbit. (Redrawn from Dawkins and Hull, *J. Physiol.*, 1964.)

the possibility of its playing a role in the heat production of the fully-grown animal is by no means ruled out, especially since the tissue is of paramount importance in many hibernating species.

Brown adipose tissue containing a lot of fat is actually yellow in colour and it becomes brown as the fat store is depleted. The colour itself is due to the presence of large quantities of mitochondrial cytochromes. The tissue is found chiefly around the neck and between the scapulae on the back, but it occurs also between the thoracic muscles and in globules around the viscera (fig. 3.14). Histologically the brown fat cell is distinguished from the white by its round, often centrally-positioned nucleus, and by the large number of small fat droplets ; white tissue is characterized by a flattened, eccentrically placed nucleus and one single large droplet of fat. Brown fat also has a much richer nerve and blood supply.

There are important specific differences in the presence or absence of the tissue. Thus it is found abundantly in the new-born rabbit, mouse, rat, sheep, cat and human infant, but appears to be absent from the pig and ox as well as from all of the birds so far examined. We shall see in a few moments how these anatomical differences are related to physiological function.

After a long period of controversy it has now been established beyond doubt that the brown fat is, in new-born animals, a major site of heat production. It is, in fact, largely responsible for the increase in meta-bolism which is often seen to occur in the absence of shivering when young animals are exposed to the cold. (It is for this reason that brown fat is most often spoken of as the centre of ' non-shivering thermo-genesis '.) Unlike the white adipose tissue, the brown should be regarded ' not merely as a simple insulating blanket, but perhaps as an electric blanket ' (G. F. Cahill). That is, it is essential for the cold-induced metabolic response not because it represents a store of energy or an insulating layer, but because it is itself a site of heat production. This is shown by the fact that the subcutaneous temperature over a sheet of brown fat is often higher than the deep body temperature (see fig. 5.12) ; furthermore, its surgical removal severely reduces the cold response. The ' electric blanket ' effect is particularly useful because there is often an intimate contact between the brown fat deposits and the large veins returning cool blood from the periphery. Thus the heat generated in the fat is applied directly to the blood as it enters the thorax, so that the vital organs are protected from cold.

In those new-born animals which possess brown fat, it is now known that the mediator of the metabolic response to cold is the hormone noradrenaline. Injections of this cause a sharp rise in heat production, which is abolished by removal of the brown fatty tissue. In natural conditions, the noradrenaline could either be borne in the blood after secretion by the adrenal medulla, or could be released at the sympathetic nerve endings close to the actual cells. Recent experiments, which include the direct stimulation of the sympathetic nerves in the rabbit's neck and the concurrent detection of a rise in temperature in the brown fat supplied by these nerves, strongly suggest that control is exerted mainly by the second mechanism.

New-born animals which do not possess brown fat fail to show the metabolic response to injections of noradrenaline, even though they do increase their heat production in the cold. In the new-born pig, injections of adrenaline are effective in accelerating metabolism, much as occurs in other animals during adulthood. The explanation of this appears to be that, in the pig, carbohydrate metabolism rather than fat metabolism is the source of increased energy production in the cold. The adrenaline activates the splitting of glycogen in liver and muscle by its influence on phosphorylase activity, so making glucose available in a form that can readily be oxidized.

The picture in birds remains somewhat confused. Since there appears to be no brown fat it is not surprising that injections of nora-drenaline in the newly hatched chicken have a negligible effect on metabolism. It appears in fact that the catecholamines can be discounted as mediators of the non-shivering metabolic response to cold which does occur ; they produce only hypothermia and sleep. Paradoxically, increased fat metabolism is a primary response to cold exposure, and there is some evidence that 5-hydroxytryptamine (5-HT) or glucagon (a pancreatic hormone) may be involved. What is important at this stage, however, is that, contrary to earlier opinion, non-shivering thermogensis has now been demonstrated in birds even though the site of the heat production—if there is a discrete site—has still to be discovered.

3.2.2. *Muscle Tone and Shivering*

When Lavoisier compared the heat production of a guinea pig as measured on the one hand by the melting of ice and on the other by its output of carbon dioxide, he was aware that a possible explanation of the small discrepancy between the results lay in the different temperatures at which the measurements were made. Later, this increased meta-bolism in the cold became the basis of Rubner's distinction between chemical and physical thermoregulation. We now include as part of the chemical response to cold both shivering and non-shivering thermo-gensis, although in short-term exposures the former is generally by far the more important. A few authors have preferred to reserve the term chemical thermogensis for cold-induced increases in the metabolic rate of tissues other than the skeletal muscles ; on this definition the heat production due to the active tremor of shivering is designated ' physical thermogenesis '. On the whole, however, there seems to be little to gain by adding to the terminology of an already overburdened subject, so we shall follow Rubner's original classification and bracket all the mechanisms of heat production together under the term chemical regulation.

The problem of separating the two components of heat production, the shivering and the non-shivering, is at least as old as this century. Opinion for or against the view that the latter plays a significant role fluctuated back and forth with each new piece of experimental evidence. With the wisdom of hindsight we can now see that the controversy raged for so long largely because, in interpreting the results of various experiments, neither the reality of specific differences nor the importance of cold-adaptation in affecting the responses of animals was fully recognized.

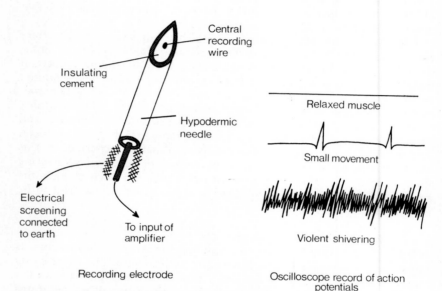

Fig. 3.15. The electromyographic technique for recording action potentials associated with muscle contraction. The frequency of the action potentials is qualitatively related to the state of activity of the muscle.

When finally it was appreciated that there might be an increase in muscle tension following exposure to cold which, however, could not be seen as overt shivering, it became clear that only an examination of the activity of the muscles themselves could resolve the question of whether any increase in heat production was due to an increase in pre-shivering muscle tone, or to an accelerated metabolism of other tissues.

66

The development of the electromyographic recording techniques (EMG) promised to provide the answer. A concentric needle electrode, insulated except for the tip, is inserted into the muscle and connected by way of a suitable amplifying system to an oscilloscope or a sensitive electronic recorder (fig. 3.15). The electrical activity (action potentials) associated with contraction of the muscle fibres can then be displayed while the animal or subject is at rest or exposed to cold. A completely relaxed muscle shows no sign of electrical activity and the record is flat. A slight movement of the muscle by voluntary or involuntary means is betrayed by the appearance of a few action potentials in the record, and the frequency with which these occur increases with increased movement. In violent shivering the electromyographic record presents a confused pattern of great activity.

This technique has now shown conclusively that increased muscle tension does in fact develop before the onset of visually detectable shivering. The increase is associated with a rise in heat production. This evidence destroys the idea that only tissues other than the muscles are involved in any pre-shivering rise of metabolism, although it does not of course eliminate the possibility that such tissues are contributing to the rise. Indeed, the same methods also demonstrate that true non-muscular thermogensis is involved, at least during long-term adaptation to cold, for over a period of several weeks the electromyographic activity, though not the metabolism, has often been observed to decline. Generally speaking, it is now considered that shivering represents the first chemical line of defence against cold, while non-shivering thermogensis is a second line of defence which operates during chronic exposure. The inevitable exception to this appears to be the cold-adapted rat, where non-shivering thermogensis is switched on and off with the same rapidity as shivering in other animals. The mechanism accounts for about 40 per cent of the rat's total heat production.

Shivering itself must be regarded as an emergency mechanism which comes into action only when insulative protection is no longer adequate. In so far as no mechanical work is performed by the trembling muscles—there is a fairly random, uncoordinated contraction of both flexors and extensors—it is an efficient means of heat production, for all the energy involved is available to keep the body warm. Nevertheless, it is not economical as a method of thermoregulation, partly because the very motion itself accelerates the loss of heat by convection and by the increased flow of blood to the superficial muscles ; it is also a very substantial drain on the body's energy resources. J. D. Hardy has expressed the ' efficiency ' of shivering in terms of the proportion of extra heat generated that is retained in the body. Thus, in an experiment conducted at 23°C, the rate of heat production without shivering was 73 W compared to a rate of heat loss of 101 W ; during a bout of shivering the heat production rose to 190 W and the rate of loss

67

of heat to 135 W. He estimated the efficiency of the shivering as:

$$\frac{\text{Heat storage rate}}{(\text{Heat production with shivering} - \text{Heat production without shivering})}$$

$$=\frac{190-135}{190-73}=0\cdot48=48 \text{ per cent.}$$

On the basis of a similar experiment involving voluntary exercise instead of shivering, the efficiency of this form of heat production was estimated to be only 20 per cent, owing to a substantial further increase in the heat lost by convection.

The heat production due to shivering in most birds and mammals results in an increase of metabolism of 2- or 3-fold over the basal rate. This resembles that due to light exercise. Maximal shivering may, in some animals however, increase metabolism by as much as five times, perhaps most notably in a creature like the armadillo where physical methods of insulation are minimal. Nevertheless, this rate of heat production still does not match that seen in severe exercise when metabolic rate can rise by up to twenty times.

One of the most notable features of shivering is that it is widely distributed among muscles—especially those of the jaw, trunk and limbs —whose normal function is under voluntary control. Thus, rather like respiration, shivering can be consciously inhibited for a limited period. Yet if the whole of the cerebral cortex (that part of the brain associated with conscious control) of an animal is removed, its shivering rhythm is unaffected and, for purposes of thermoregulation at any rate, the shivering activities of the muscles are under autonomic control only. The primary control centre lies in the posterior part of the hypo-thalamus, and from here numerous links run through the mid- and hind-brains, down the lateral columns of the spinal cord and out to the muscles by way of the ventral roots. The interesting thing about the pathway in the spinal cord is that it differs from the tract of fibres which organizes voluntary movements of the very same muscles as engage in shivering. This is the anatomical explanation underlying the ability of some patients suffering localized damage to the cord to shiver with muscles that are paralysed for voluntary movement. The dual innerva-tion is also shown by the fact that shivering is generally suppressed during voluntary activity of a muscle (which means, incidentally, that the heat production by the two means are not additive). Other features in the nervous regulation of shivering are discussed in Chapter 6.

3.2.3.1. *The mechanism of heat production in muscle*

We have seen that any increase in the tension of muscle fibres, whether or not it is recognizable as movement to the naked eye, is responsible for the generation of body warmth. Thus athletes and ballet dancers 'warm up' before a performance in the belief that this increases the efficiency of their work (presumably by speeding the rate of chemical reactions). In so doing they recognize two distinct categories of energy associated with muscle, namely heat and work. The first law of thermodynamics says that energy can neither be created nor destroyed ; this also implies that when one form of energy is converted to another, it goes over in exact equivalents so that the sum total remains constant. In the body it is easy to convert work into heat but impossible to convert heat into work. This is in accordance with the second law of thermodynamics, which demands that in order to perform the latter conversion, as occurs for example in a steam engine, there must be a steep thermal gradient ; in the body the muscles have to function at a fairly uniform temperature. Because of the irreversability of the conversion of energy in the muscles, any free energy that is not successfully converted into mechanical work must be degraded into heat ; so far as the work itself is concerned, this is therefore a measure of the inefficiency of the process.

The machinery of the muscle uses adenosine triphosphate as its fuel. The machine operates by means of the same series of enzyme reactions as we have already encountered in outline. The processes of glycolysis, of the tricarboxylic acid cycle, and of the cytochrome chain combine together in the production of adenosine triphosphate, and the contractile proteins of the muscle break this down and transfer part of its energy into mechanical work and part into heat. Adenosine triphosphate is the only substance that the contractile mechanism can use directly, but since there is only about 3 mmol kg^{-1} in most muscle—energy for about eight contractions only—the adenosine triphosphate that is broken down during contraction is quickly regenerated by energy from phosphocreatine (PC) and ultimately, of course, from the oxidation of glucose. (Under anaerobic conditions, such as often occur during heavy exercise, energy is made available to the muscle by the hydrolysis of glycogen to lactic acid.) Muscle contraction, then, involves the reaction :

$$ATP \rightleftharpoons ADP + \text{inorganic P} + \text{energy}.$$

This is catalysed by one of the muscle proteins acting as an enzyme (ATP-ase). But the adenosine triphosphate is rapidly replenished thus :

$$ADP + PC \rightleftharpoons ATP + C$$

the enzyme responsible here being known simply as creatine phosphotransferase.

Details of the actual process of heat production as such are complicated and require an acquaintance with thermoelectric techniques of a rather specialized kind which need not concern us here. Briefly, what is called the initial heat is produced by active contraction of the muscle, and an approximately equal quantity—the recovery heat—is subsequently generated during the period while the muscle recovers in oxygen. When a muscle is contracting isotonically (that is, with a change in length but none in tension) it produces more heat than when it contracts isometrically (with a change in tension but none in length). However, since mechanical work is usually defined as the distance through which a load is moved, the muscle performs no work during a strictly isometric contraction and all the energy would be degraded as heat.

The relation between chemical energy and heat in muscle is governed by the law of the conservation of energy. Over a fixed time interval, if only one reaction is involved, the conventional equation is :

$$\text{Heat} + \text{work} = n(-\Delta H) \text{ joule}$$

where n is the number of moles of reaction and ΔH is the heat of the reaction (the change in the heat per unit mass). Because the reaction gives out heat the sign is negative : the system is losing heat to the environment. (For any exothermic reaction the number ΔH is negative, so that $-\Delta H$ is actually positive.) The efficiency of most muscles in transforming chemical energy into mechanical work over the whole process of contraction and recovery is of the order of 20–25 per cent. It has not yet proved technically possible to measure the efficiency of contraction alone.

3.2.4. *Voluntary Activity*

The level of activity or the rate of exercise markedly affects the energy output and this is reflected in the metabolic rate. The metabolism of work varies directly with the work performed and this is usually measured as the product of the force and the distance moved. When the work consists merely of moving the body, the metabolic rate therefore varies directly as the mass.

Exercise metabolism in man is often measured under controlled conditions by means of a bicycle ergometer. In its simplest form this consists of a stationary bicycle fitted with a mechanical friction brake which acts on the wheel. The work performed is then calculated by measuring the ' path ' cycled in metres and multiplying this by the weight on the brake. (The rate of work has traditionally been expressed in kilopond metre per minute, where 1 kp is the force acting on a mass of 1 kg at normal gravity. Now, however, we use watt.) Provided that the work is performed at a fixed speed, which is usually achieved by pedalling in time with a metronome, the metabolism can then be compared for different levels of work, say by using an open-circuit method of respiration calorimetry. The rise in metabolism is found to be roughly 25 per cent of the parallel rise in work performed, this giving an estimate of muscular efficiency.

The great bulk of the work on exercise metabolism has been performed on man. Heat production is minimal during sleep, usually about 75 W, whereas just sitting at rest may increase this to 115 W. The maximum rate of physical effort that could be maintained for about an hour might then be expected to lie somewhere between 600 and 1200 W, although for periods of a few minutes even higher levels are possible. At such times, up to 90 per cent of the body's total heat production may be contributed by the exercising muscles, compared to about 20 per cent at rest.

CHAPTER 4
physiological regulation of heat loss

THE natural physical exchange of heat between the living body and its environment is influenced to a very large degree by two physiological mechanisms, namely, alteration of the conductance of the superficial tissues by changes in the amount of blood flowing through them, and alteration in the rate of evaporation of water from the general body surface or from the respiratory tract. The first of these operates essentially by changing the thermal gradient between the body surface and the environment, thus accelerating or diminishing the flow of heat down the gradient. The second operates by raising the vapour pressure gradient. In the zone of thermoneutrality, almost all of the physiological regulation of body temperature may be performed by changes in the skin temperature brought about by alterations in blood flow, but above the upper critical temperature the evaporative loss of heat becomes progressively more important until, when the average skin temperature equals the temperature of the environment, no further direct transfer is possible from the body and evaporation is then the sole remaining channel.

Below the critical temperature both evaporative heat loss and tissue conductance soon reach minimum levels and can be reduced no further, so that when we speak of physical regulation we most often have in mind the mechanisms which facilitate the loss of heat from the body during exposure to warm conditions. However, we should also remember that it is during cold exposure that the body makes maximum use of both physical and physiological devices which can assist in retaining heat, and that it is only when these become inadequate that chemical regulation comes to the rescue. These devices are no less a part of physical regulation because they operate in the cold rather than in the heat, and we might reasonably begin our discussion at this point before going on to the larger subject of how animals accelerate the loss of heat in a hot environment.

4.1. *THE PERIPHERAL CIRCULATION*

4.1.1. *Physiology of Counter-current Heat Exchange*
Even in a large homoiotherm it is obviously not possible to provide all parts of the body with equally effective insulation if freedom of movement is not to be curtailed. We know that the limbs are typically much

more labile in temperature than is the core of the body, and that because heat loss depends on the temperature difference between the body surface and the environment, the reduction of temperature in the shell tissues is the only way that the thermal homoiostasis of the core can be maintained in conditions when heat dissipation is rapid. While radial gradients of temperature (from the centre of the trunk or limbs outwards to the surface) always occur, many animals use a counter-current heat exchange system to establish longitudinal gradients as well. The principle of this is exactly the same as that employed in some forms of boiler, where the hot exhaust gases are used to pre-heat the cold incoming air (thus increasing the overall efficiency of the boiler's output) simply by arranging the outlet and inlet pipes in close parallel formation. In the body the system works as follows (fig. 4.1).

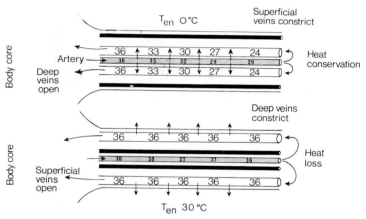

Fig. 4.1. Diagrammatic representation of the counter-current heat exchange system operating in the body. Constricted veins in black. Arrows show direction of blood flow.

In cool conditions, when the conservation of body heat is important, the superficial veins in the skin of the limbs constrict, thus presenting a greatly increased resistance to the flow of blood which, as a result, is directed into the deeper vessels lying in close apposition to the arteries that supply the appendage. By this means the blood leaving the core is able to transfer a large proportion of its heat down the thermal gradient to the cool blood returning from the periphery. Consequently, blood actually reaching the heart has suffered little drop from core temperature, even though adequate supplies have been provided for the functional needs of the extremities. The great advantage of a really effective counter-current system is that it permits a substantial flow of blood from the warm interior of the body to the cool surface, yet with small external loss of heat. Without such controlled heat transfer the blood

F

supply to the periphery would have to be reduced drastically, with the inevitable loss in functional efficiency of the extremities. Some of the best developed heat exchange systems incorporate, in the place of parallel axial vessels, complex networks of small arteries and veins (called *retia* ; *rete*, singular) which provide a greatly enhanced area of contact across which conductive heat transfer can occur. Networks of this kind are known in many species of homoiotherm, perhaps most notably in the long bare legs of wading and aquatic birds ; alternatively, as in the flippers of many whales, the large arteries may be completely surrounded by pools of venous blood which also allow for the maximum exchange of heat.

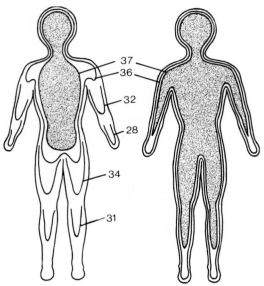

Fig. 4.2. Diagram of the effects of counter-current heat exchange in the human body exposed to cold conditions (left) and warm conditions (right). The isotherms (in °C) show that the core shrinks in the cold leaving a peripheral shell of cooler tissue. (Redrawn from Aschoff and Wever, *Naturwiss.*, 1958.)

Conservation of heat by this method would obviously not be desirable in hot weather, especially in well-insulated animals or during exercise. Under such circumstances the mechanism is therefore shut down by the simple expedient of constricting the deep axial veins and dilating the superficial ones. Much of the blood then passes close to the surface on its way back to the core and the loss of heat to the surroundings is maximal. A good example of the effectiveness of counter-current heat exchange is provided by some species of gulls and herons. During winter the steep longitudinal thermal gradients which exist in the unfeathered legs of these birds restrict the loss of heat, even to the cold water of the northern winter, to less than 10 per cent of the total metabolism. In hot conditions, the non-operation of the exchange system allows these same appendages to mediate the loss of almost the entire heat produced. Nothing so dramatic can be demonstrated in man, although temperature in the arteries of the arm may fall by 0.03 K mm^{-1} as a result of heat transfer to venous blood. This results in marked longitudinal gradients (fig. 4.2).

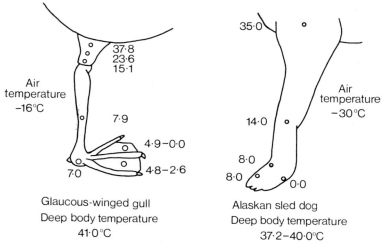

Fig. 4.3. Subcutaneous temperatures (in °C) on the extremities of a gull and a dog exposed to cold. (Redrawn from Irving and Krog, *J. appl. Physiol.*, 1955.)

As a result of the longitudinal thermal gradients set up by the heat exchange system, the tissues at the extremities of some homoiotherms may be more than 30 K below the temperature of the body core (fig. 4.3). We do not, however, regard such regional heterothermy as a failure of thermoregulation, and the reasonableness of this view is borne out by various adaptations that are to be found in peripheral tissues that allow their continual function at these low temperatures. A well-known example is provided by the herring gull (*Larus argentatus*). In birds adapted to winter temperatures, different segments of the long tibial nerve directly connecting the feet to the spinal cord are sensitive to different temperatures. Thus a section of the nerve taken from a feathered part of the leg, where temperature never falls below 33°C, is unable to conduct impulses at below 11·7°C. A section from the unfeathered part of the leg, however, where temperatures are usually between 6 and 13°C, will continue to conduct at as low as 2·8°C. This sort of adaptation presumably permits normal use of the feet even when the gulls are walking on ice or swimming in water at near freezing temperatures. Another example is the difference between the melting point of samples of body fat taken from the interior of the body or from the extremities of the caribou (*Rangifer tarandus*). That from the hoof melts at near 0°C, more than 30 K below the melting point of core fat, giving it a softness even in severe conditions which would be a valuable aid to flexibility of the feet.

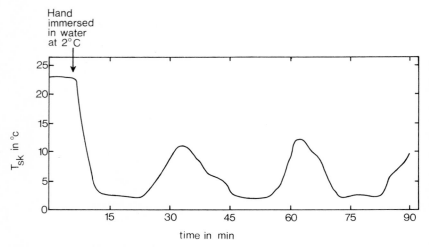

Fig. 4.4. Cold-vasodilatation as seen in the human hand. The curve shows the response of skin temperature (T_{sk}) plotted against time.

Another adaptation appropriate to regional heterothermy is the special form of thermoregulatory control directed towards the protection of the tissues from damage by freezing. A good example is the phenomenon of cold vasodilatation. If you immerse a hand or foot in water at a few degrees above freezing, while the skin temperature is continuously recorded, you will see at first a rapid fall to near the water temperature, indicating maximal constriction of the skin vessels. If the cold exposure is continued for about 15 minutes, however, there is a spontaneous re-warming by 10 K or more, followed by a second decline and then a rise, and so on, in a rhythmic manner often referred to as the 'hunting reaction' (fig. 4.4). Similar responses have been described in the foot of the domestic fowl and in the rabbit's ear. In man, at least, there is evidence that the vasodilatation and increased blood flow which underlie the rise in temperature have local protective

76

value, even though frostbite may still develop during the periods of cooling. This may be explained in terms of natural selection by saying that it is less disadvantageous for the shell to be damaged than for the temperature of the core to drop.

4.1.2. *Anatomy of the Dermal Blood Vessels*

An examination of the vascular supply to the skin provides a structural explanation for the changes of blood flow seen in cold vasodilatation. Throughout the superficial layers of the dermis there is an exceptionally rich system of capillary loops which are supplied from arteries and arterioles in the deeper part of the dermis ; they empty their blood into large, thin-walled vessels of the venous plexus. It is, in fact, the venous side of the skin circulation which contains the greater part of the blood found in the skin.

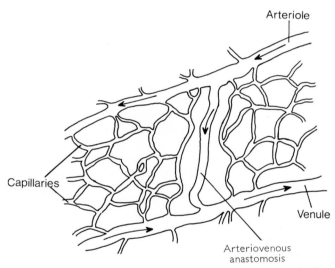

Fig. 4.5. The capillary bed in the skin of the extremities. Both the arterioles and the arteriovenous anastomoses are well endowed with circular smooth muscle under nervous control. When an anastomosis opens, the arteriolar muscle immediately beyond its opening contracts to shut down the capillary network.

A special feature of the skin of the extremities, notably in the digits of man's hands and feet, in the webbed feet of gulls and ducks and in the ears of many mammals, is the prominence of vascular channels, called arteriovenous anastomoses, which form direct connexions between the arterioles and venules of the dermis, thus by-passing the capillaries (fig. 4.5). The vessels are muscular and particularly well supplied with nerve endings. They have two functions : first, the local protection of the exposed extremities from damage due to low temperature by allowing their periodic flooding with warm blood (as we have seen in cold vasodilatation), and second, a more general role in the maintenance of body temperature during neutral and warm conditions by means of their ability to alter rapidly the amount of blood flowing in the extremities. This influences the skin temperature and the thermal gradient to the environment.

4.1.3. *Vasomotor Changes in Relation to Ambient Temperature*

During exposure to heat or in exercise, the main burden of maintaining heat balance in the body is borne by the circulatory system. Even under basal conditions at neutral ambient temperature, the heat of metabolism has still to be dissipated to the environment, and we can readily see that transportation of heat from the interior of the body to the body surface is one of the principal homoiostatic functions of the blood stream. An increased flow of blood through the working muscles not only satisfies their local metabolic needs but also carries away the excess heat generated. An increased flow to the skin cools the warm blood and, in some mammals, also supplies water to the sweat glands. At the same time there may a concurrent increase in the flow to the alimentary canal for the transfer of water from there to the skin. Clearly then, a considerable strain is quickly imposed on the circulation during heat stress, and this is met by an increase up to five-fold in the output of the heart and by compensatory reductions in the flow of blood to regions of the body not directly concerned in the production of excess heat, or incapable of dissipating it to the environment.

In this context we can see why it is that the blood supply to the skin is often said to be the servant of the body's temperature requirements rather than of the skin itself. The skin is a major organ of the temperature-regulating system, not only in naked animals like man, but also in heavily furred or feathered creatures, which commonly have ' heat-windows ' of poorly insulated skin in the extremities which can be opened on demand when there is danger of over-heating. Despite this general rule, we should not lose sight of the fact that there are circumstances when the local needs of the skin may dominate those of temperature regulation as a whole. We have already seen one example in cold vasodilatation, when valuable body heat is lost in an attempt to minimize tissue destruction. Another would be the high local blood flow required for wound healing after mechanical injury.

The regulation of blood flow to appendages such as limbs and ears has been studied far more than that to other areas of the body, chiefly because projecting parts lend themselves more readily to the experimental methods available. These include various types of calorimetry, where the appendage is immersed in water and an estimate made of the

78

blood flow in terms of the rate at which heat is transferred from the appendage to the water. Because of phenomena such as counter-current heat exchange this approach is difficult to calibrate ; that is, there is often only a rough, qualitative relationship between the rate of heat loss and the rate of blood flow. A somewhat more satisfactory method is that called venous occlusion plethysmography, in which the organ is enclosed in a fluid-filled chamber (the plethysmograph) with its one opening connected to a volume recorder (fig. 4.6). Changes in the

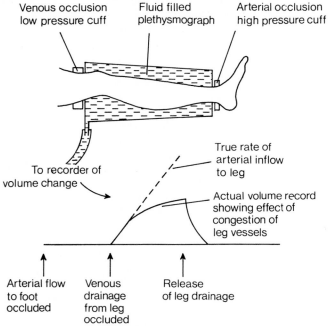

Fig. 4.6. The technique of venous occlusion plethysmography as applied to the human leg. Inflation of the arterial pressure cuff to 250 mm Hg (about 33 kPa) prevents blood flowing to or from the foot. Inflation of the venous cuff to 30 mm Hg (4 kPa) prevents venous drainage without affecting arterial inflow. The initial rate of change of volume is therefore a measure of this flow.

volume of the organ due to alterations of blood flow are then measured ; when the venous drainage from the organ is occluded by a pneumatic cuff which leaves the high pressure arterial supply unaffected, the increase in volume which follows must be due to arterial inflow alone. Naturally, this is true only during the first few seconds, after which the record flattens out as congestion of the vessels begins and the veins are forced to dilate and take up the excess blood.

With suitable precautions the plethysmographic technique can give reasonably accurate estimates of total blood flow to the appendage, but it still cannot separate the flow to the muscles from that to the skin. For the study of temperature relations it is important to know by which route heat from the body's interior is transported to the extremities. Several methods have been used in an attempt to overcome this difficulty. One involves measurements of the oxygen contents of the blood draining the muscles and the skin respectively ; an increase in the oxygen is assumed to be due to vasodilatation and increased blood flow. Another attempts to shut down the skin circulation by infiltrating adrenaline to constrict the vessels ; any flow changes which remain must be due to vessels deep in the muscles. None of these methods is without its limitations, but by combining several of them it has been shown that the enhanced blood flow that accompanies body heating is due almost entirely to the increase in that through the skin.

There is now an abundance of evidence that vasomotor control of the circulation can result in enormous variability in cutaneous flow. In the extremities the maximum blood flow attainable is commonly 80–100 times the minimum, while in the human fingertips the variation may be up to 200-fold. The quantity of heat thus carried to the surface by convective transfer in the blood may be very great, although it is important to realize that changes in thermal conductance are often much less than those in blood flow because of counter-current exchange. In naked man, dilatation of the skin vessels rarely occurs below about 26–28°C ; at lower ambient temperatures constriction is maximal, and the vascular convection of heat to the surface is at its lowest level, so that active regulation of body temperature by the skin is then insignificant. In fully vasoconstricted skin the total blood flow may be of the order of 0.25 cm^3 m^{-2} s^{-1} ; at 35°C air temperature and moderate activity this may rise to more than 3.3 cm^3 m^{-2} s^{-1}, and during severe exercise to 20 cm^3 m^{-2} s^{-1}, an increase of 80-fold.

Many other animals rely much more on the passive protection provided by fur or feathers, and dramatic changes in skin vasomotor activity, like those in man, are not found, at least over the body surface as a whole. For example, the contribution to the control of heat loss exerted by the vessels of the feathered skin in the fowl appears to be negligible, although in the naked skin of the head and legs there is evidence of a strong thermoregulatory role. Again, in the dog the increase in blood flow at high temperatures occurs chiefly in the tongue and buccal cavity, not in the extremities or over the general body surface. Differences such as these generally make good sense in thermoregulatory terms ; in man heat loss by direct and indirect transfer occurs from all over the body surface, whereas in animals like the fowl and dog evaporative cooling occurs chiefly from the upper respiratory tract.

The temperature of a terrestrial animal's skin at a given moment is influenced to a major degree by the rate of blood flowing through it. It is also affected by the temperature of the arterial blood reaching the surface, especially in the extremities where, as we have seen, this may be much cooler than the central body temperature. Other influential factors include the temperature, humidity and movement of the air, the radiant heat exchange with the environment, and the rate of evaporation of moisture from the skin surface. Under terrestrial conditions there is therefore seldom a simple relationship between blood flow and skin temperature.

In the aquatic animal the temperature of the skin surface is essentially that of the water itself, because the rate at which heat is carried to or from the skin by the water is immensely greater than the rate at which it can be transported to the skin by the blood. If the skin is covered with fur or, in man, by fabric, its temperature then reflects the ratio of the thermal insulation between the body core and the skin on the one hand and that between the skin and the water on the other. The first of these is closely dependent on the rate of flow of blood to the skin.

4.1.4. *Autonomic Nervous Regulation of the Skin Circulation*

It has been known for a long time that the skin vessels over all parts of the body dilate in hot conditions and constrict in cool, and there has been a great deal of argument as to the details of their control. Almost a hundred years ago the Belgian Léon Frédéricq (1851–1935) suggested three possible mechanisms by which the vascular responses might operate. First, autonomic activity of the vasomotor centre of the hind brain might be regulated by the temperature of the blood flowing through it; the diameter of the skin vessels would then be said to be under central control. Secondly, the vasomotor centre might be triggered into action as a result of the activity of temperature-sensitive nerve endings situated in the skin; this would be called reflex control. Finally, there might be a direct regulation of the musculature of the skin vessels themselves, operating according to local changes of temperature; this would be local control. In Chapter 6 we shall consider some of the evidence that has accumulated since Frédéricq's time in favour of each of these points of view, but it is appropriate here to outline a few of the experiments which have a specific bearing on our understanding of vasomotor activity in the skin.

Much of the controversy that still surrounds this subject has resulted from generalizations drawn from too few experiments. However, there is now a solid body of evidence concerning the role of the various possible mechanisms and several of the significant experiments can readily be performed in the classroom or laboratory. Thus, in man, plunging one arm into warm water is followed after a few minutes by a massive vasodilatation (seen as flushing) and increase in the temperature of the opposite hand. That the response is too slow to be a nervous reflex from temperature receptors in the skin is shown by the fact that the effect is blocked if a pressure cuff is maintained around the top of the immersed arm so as to arrest its circulation. This cuff can be kept inflated indefinitely (with brief releases to give the limb a change of blood) without any vasodilatation in the opposite hand. Following release of the cuff a normal vasodilatation occurs after 5–10 minutes, just as before. This experiment is interpreted as showing that the response in the opposite hand depends upon the return of warm blood from the extremities to the central nervous system ; that is, the effect seems to be under central control. However, other experiments conflict to some extent with this one, and should remind us to take great care before formulating any general rules of physiological function. For example, warming the legs with infra-red heat from a radiant lamp causes a marked vasodilatation in the hands almost at once, too quickly, that is, for any blood-borne effect. This can be proved by showing that pneumatic cuffs placed around the legs have no effect on the response, which must therefore be relayed reflexly from receptors in the skin. Both central and reflex control appear to play a part.

Repetition of the first experiment with cold water instead of warm shows that the two mechanisms may function in an additive manner. Immersing an arm in the water with the circulation arrested is followed by a rapid reflex vasoconstriction in the opposite hand which, however, is transient, for it wears off after a short while even though the immersion is maintained. If the pressure cuff is now released, there is at first no effect, but after a few minutes a sustained vasoconstriction occurs as the cooled blood appears to act on temperature receptors in the brain.

Less is known for certain about the role played by Frédéricq's third possible mechanism, that of local vasomotor control, partly because it is always difficult to be certain that all nervous influences have been eliminated. Nevertheless, most investigators have found that the local effects of temperature on a limb which lacks any connexion with the sympathetic nervous system are, after an initial period of maximum vasodilatation, in no essential way different from those in the same limb when intact. Thus there is a normal increase in local blood flow with temperature, and the response of cold vasodilatation also appears to be normal.

A possible explanation for these rather unexpected local effects may lie in the phenomenon of the 'axon reflex'. The activation of a temperature-sensitive nerve ending in the skin results in impulses passing in the direction of the spinal cord which, instead of generating a normal reflex through the central nervous system, send impulses in the opposite direction to normal ('anti-dromically') down other branches of the same nerve fibre to sensory receptors on or near the skin arterioles (fig. 4.7). Then, some chemical transmitter substance, possibly adenosine triphosphate, is released in the neighbourhood of the arterioles, causing dilatation just as if the normal sympathetic innervation had been intact. The axon reflex occurs after the local sensory nerves are severed, but it disappears as these degenerate. Evidence in favour of the mechanism is that stimulation of the peripheral ends of several sensory nerves can cause dilatation in the corresponding skin areas. Evidence against it is that some local vasodilator responses are believed to occur even after total denervation of the area (that is, not after sympathetic denervation alone). From these considerations alone you will see how difficult it is to isolate a controlling mechanism with absolute assurance.

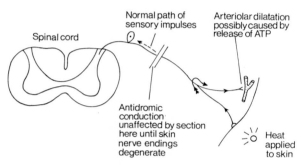

Fig. 4.7. Diagram of the axon reflex ; a possible explanation of local vasomotor activity in the skin.

Another area of controversy is the mechanism of control over dilatation of the blood vessels in the skin. Is there an interruption of the continuous ' tonic ' restraining activity of nerves which normally cause constriction, or are there distinct nerves which actively cause dilatation ? Ever since Claude Bernard's demonstration in 1851 that section of the sympathetic nerve chain in the neck of the rabbit caused flushing of the ear on the same side, while stimulation of the chain caused pallor, it has been universally recognized that the sympathetic nerves contain vasoconstrictor fibres which under most circumstances keep the skin vessels in a partially constricted state. A similar result to Bernard's is obtained in man if the sympathetic supply to the hands and feet is blocked by local anaesthetic ; blood flow increases and there is a rise in skin temperature. Warming the whole body also causes dilatation of the hand and foot blood vessels, but the interesting thing here is that the increase in flow is no greater than that caused by blocking the sympathetic nerves. This sort of experiment is interpreted as indicating that dilatation in the human hand and foot is due to the passive withdrawal of vasoconstrictor tone, and that there is no active vasodilatation.

83

In the forearm a somewhat different result is obtained. Blocking the sympathetic supply again leads to dilatation synchronously with that in the hand, and an increased blood flow, but the increase is not so great as that caused by heating the whole body (fig. 4.8). The greater forearm response to heat, occurring when hand blood flow is already maximal,

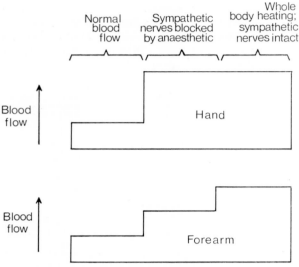

Fig. 4.8. A qualitative illustration of the different blood flow patterns in human hand and forearm following blockade of the sympathetic nerves and heating of the whole body. In the hand, increase in flow is the same in either case, indicating the withdrawal of constrictor tone only. In the arm, the increase is greater during heating, suggesting that active vasodilatation must also be involved.

cannot therefore result only from withdrawal of sympathetic constrictor impulses but must also involve active vasodilatation. Further support for this explanation is that warming of the body induces a greater blood flow in an intact arm than in an arm subjected to sympathetic blockade.

In a sweating animal, such as man, massive cutaneous dilatation caused by heat would normally be accompanied by the secretion of moisture on to the skin surface. If the sweat is to be evaporated, as much heat as possible must be transported to the surface in the blood-stream, for some 600 cm³ of blood are required to bring sufficient heat to the surface to evaporate just 1 g of sweat when the temperature of the skin is 1 K below the core temperature. Sweating is effective therefore only when accompanied by maximal dilatation of the skin vessels. In this connexion it is interesting that the sweat glands themselves are believed to liberate an enzyme that acts on the proteins of the tissue fluid to form a polypeptide called bradykinin, a substance with strong vasodilator qualities. Perfusion of the skin of the forearm with saline has shown not only the presence of bradykinin, but also its increased formation with body heating. What is more, the increase can be detected before the local increase in blood flow and skin temperature, and also before the onset of sweating. This observation, together with the fact that maximal vasodilatation in the forearm occurs after that in the hand, may indicate that the second phase seen in the forearm is the result of a process incorporating several stages, the last but one of which is the release of bradykinin. If this explanation is correct it might be that a local mechanism could produce vasodilatation without the need for nervous control. This difficulty has yet to be satisfactorily resolved.

We need not spend a great deal of time in considering the anatomy and physiology of the central control of tone in the blood vessels, because relatively little is yet known about precisely how the system works. There have been many experiments involving stimulation of the brain, but it is doubtful if these have provided much information on how the mechanisms function in nature. Suffice it to say that in the medulla of the hind brain there is a group of neurones which functions in some way by collecting together information on the state and needs of the entire cardiovascular system, and by organizing changes in the output of the heart and in the diameter of the vessels such that the needs of the body in relation to its thermal state are met. Thermal information of relevance to the circulatory system reaches the brain from all over the body, and the effector mechanisms which perform the appropriate responses are controlled by way of the autonomic nervous system. This system is to a large degree under the control of the hypothalamus, and when we realize that this structure probably has a direct influence on the medullary vasomotor neurones themselves, we begin to see that the reason for our ignorance of central nervous organization lies in its immense complexity.

4.1.5. *Compensatory Adjustments*

We have also very little genuine information on how the body as a whole manages to cope with the rapid changes in demand that result from thermoregulatory adjustments to the circulation. The vascular system of the abdominal viscera certainly represents the body's chief reservoir for blood, and since both the arteries and veins are amply supplied with vasoconstrictor nerve fibres they are well suited for this role. Most probably, general visceral constriction accompanies the dilatation in the skin during heat stress or exercise, and splanchnic dilatation ensues when blood is withdrawn from the skin in the cold. In many animals, including man and the dog, the reservoir represented by the hepatic portal system, together with its subsidiary branches in

85

the spleen, can, when fully dilated, accommodate up to a third of the body's total blood volume.

4.2. EVAPORATION FROM THE RESPIRATORY TRACT

4.2.1. Fundamentals of Heat Exchange in the Respiratory Tract

The passage of air in and out of the respiratory tract of a homoio-therm results in the passive loss, under the great majority of natural environmental conditions, of a certain amount of body heat as the inspired air is raised from ambient temperature to core temperature and is saturated with water vapour. Most investigations on man have shown that the quantity of heat lost by these routes represents a small but not insignificant proportion of the total. If, for example, the average man raises the temperature of the air he breathes from 20 to 37°C, and ventilates his lungs at the rate of $500 \, l \, h^{-1}$, we can calculate, from the mass and specific heat capacity of this quantity of air, that he will lose heat at the rate of about 2·8 W by this means.

The loss due to saturating the air tends to be rather more important. Under neutral or warm conditions, air is expired from the human respiratory tract at about 35°C with a vapour tension of approximately 5·6 kPa. Obviously the vapour tension of the inspired air varies with atmospheric conditions, although it is generally between 0·65 and 2·0 kPa, so that from the difference in the amount of water carried in and out we can estimate that an average of about 12 g might be lost per hour, equivalent to a rate of heat loss of about 8 W.

The sum total, then, of the losses from warming and humidifying the inspired air might normally account for up to 10 per cent of the total metabolic heat production in man under conditions that we should consider comfortable. At 0°C, however, about 20 per cent of the heat losses are by these routes. Even so, this increase is less than we might have expected, the reason being that at very low ambient temperatures there is a fall in the temperature of the expired air which, for instance, reaches 29°C at 5°C ambient, and 26°C at − 30°C. As the inspired air is cooled it gives up heat to the respiratory surfaces during its approach to the outside ; in addition, some of the water is returned to the body by condensation on the cooled surfaces. This, as you may have noted, is a form of counter-current heat exchange exactly the same in principle as that described in connexion with the vascular system, and it is much better developed as a method of heat and water economy in some small animals than in man. In the desert-dwelling kangaroo rat (*Dipodomys merriami*), for instance, and in several species of bird, the upper respiratory passages are more suited anatomically for this type of exchange, and the temperature of the expired air is closer to that of the environment than to that of the body core. During the night, at a temperature of 15°C and 25 per cent relative humidity, the system enables the kangaroo rat and the cactus wren (*Campylorhynchus brunneicapillum*) to recover on exhalation no less than 88 per cent and 75 per cent respectively of the heat added to the air on inspiration. This represents a saving of 16 per cent of metabolic heat production in each case.

During hot conditions or after exercise, the natural evaporative losses which occur as an inevitable consequence of the breathing movements have been developed in most of the birds so far investigated, and in many mammals, into the chief means of heat dissipation. Control over the rate of evaporation is achieved by varying the volume of the air ventilating the respiratory tract. This increase typically takes the form of rapid shallow breathing, as is seen in a panting animal such as the dog, rather than by slow but deep breathing which, so far as heat loss is concerned, might be expected to achieve the same ends. The panting respiration allows for maximal ventilation of the upper sections of the respiratory passages (buccal cavity, nasal pathways, tongue and trachea) without unduly increasing the exchange of air occurring in the lung itself. We shall examine the importance of this adaptation later on ; here it is sufficient to note that panting is, after all, only a modification of the mechanical breathing movements whose first job is to ventilate the lungs, bringing oxygen to the gas-exchange surfaces and washing out the carbon dioxide. This function has to continue unabated even when the secondary function of promoting heat loss is added to it.

4.2.2. *The Origins of Panting*

Before considering the physiology of panting we might look briefly at the use and distribution of this form of heat loss mechanism among present day animals, to see if this throws any light on its possible development during the progression of the vertebrate line. The first thing that we have to realize is that panting is not restricted solely to the endothermic vertebrates. In a rudimentary form at least, it is present in many species of desert-living lizards, where there is good evidence that it may have a genuine biological significance both in prolonging the period during which the animal can stay abroad in the hot sun, and as a last protective measure against the dangers of lethal over-heating. This suggests to us that primitive panting may have been used by reptiles before the mammals and birds appeared on the scene, and also that it may have preceded sweating (that is, actively controlled evaporation from the skin as distinct from passive diffusion) in the mammalian line. This argument may be supported to some extent by the fact that efficient open-mouthed panting is common among the marsupials, while sweating has been described in only one species.

In the placental mammals panting has been described in most orders, although in some, notably the rodents, it is at best poorly developed and is often absent altogether. In either event, the chief means of evaporative cooling in these animals is by profuse salivation and licking of the coat and limbs. The moisture evaporates from the surface of the fur rather than from the skin itself, and this means that a large proportion of the heat of vaporization is taken from the ambient air ; such a form of cooling is consequently inefficient, and it is not surprising that rodents tend to rely heavily on behavioural methods of thermoregulation.

Among many of the more advanced terrestrial mammals the responsibility for evaporative cooling is shared to a greater or lesser extent with the sweating mechanism. It is possible to arrange various species in some sort of order on this basis without, however, implying any obvious phylogenetic significance. Thus the dog—and the pig, contrary to popular belief—appear to have little or no active sweating capability and, at least when behavioural regulation is blocked, they rely on evaporative losses from the respiratory tract. Sheep lose eight to ten times as much moisture by panting as from the skin, although thermoregulatory sweating does occur. Cattle, on the other hand, lose 85 per cent of their evaporated water from the sweat glands and only the remainder by panting. Finally, in man (although so-called panting has been induced in thoroughly unnatural circumstances like submergence of all but the face in a hot bath) the sweating mechanism alone accounts for all of the heat produced by metabolism even when this is raised by several times or when all direct heat transfer is eliminated by high environmental temperature.

In birds, many of the unique features of body structure and function appear to be influenced by the development of the ability to fly. This may be the main reason why there is no regulated evaporative cooling except from the respiratory tract ; a sweating skin and the resultant dampness of the feathers would upset the fundamental flight characteristics of the plumage. Panting is therefore practically universal and has some peculiar features that make it of special interest.

4.2.3. *Respiratory Changes of Panting*

The most obvious characteristic of panting as a form of respiration is that it involves a marked quickening of the breathing movements. Even casual observation sometimes shows that each breath is considerably shallower than those seen during normal breathing at rest. As has been mentioned, this reduction in the volume of air passed in and out at each breath reduces the overall increase in the total ventilation (that is, the volume of air taken at each breath multiplied by the number of breaths per unit time) and serves to protect the lungs against too great a washing-out of carbon dioxide, and the hazards that would follow. In the dog, for example, the frequency of breathing increases by more than ten-fold during panting, but because of a great reduction in the volume of each of these breaths, the total ventilation may be no more than doubled. Under severe heat conditions this very economy of ventilation may conflict with the requirement for maximum evaporative cooling—a function which increases linearly with total ventilation—and the compromise solution which is adopted typically results in a marked but tolerable elevation of body temperature on the one hand and a marked but tolerable disturbance to the blood chemistry on the other (see below).

A feature of panting in the dog and in many birds is that an abrupt shift of respiratory frequency occurs from the resting level directly to the panting level without any gradual acceleration. This phenomenon has been best studied in the dog, where the selected panting frequency is about 320 breaths per minute. This happens to be very close to the frequency at which the entire thorax of the dog vibrates if it is treated as a natural oscillating physical system, and it is therefore almost certainly the frequency at which energy expenditure, and hence heat production, would be minimal. Strangely, this so-called 'resonant panting' has not been described in other mammals, although in birds it is quite common and probably contributes to the high level of efficiency of a species such as the pigeon where the natural frequency is about 650 per minute.

The normal thoracic movements of panting are supplemented in some birds by an oscillating hyoid apparatus which vibrates the floor of the buccal cavity. This gular flutter, as it is called, causes an efficient ventilation of the buccal region and is believed to play a major role in the heat economy of the species using it. It is a separate mechanism, separately evolved, and may be commoner than panting in the class as a whole. In the pelican, movements of the greatly expanded gular pouch are very obvious, but they occur less conspicuously in many other species too, often at the same frequency as the main respiratory movements. There is much variation, however, so that while synchronous panting and flutter may be seen in species such as the domestic fowl and pigeon, the two movements are out of phase in the white pelican, and flutter is absent altogether from passerine species. Furthermore, since the thoracic and gular movements occur together in the pigeon it is assumed that the natural vibrating frequency of the hyoid apparatus in this species must be appropriately in tune with the thorax. In the fowl the two are also in tune, but there is no resonant frequency and both increase in rate as body temperature rises. The pelican is different again ; here the gular flutter shifts abruptly to its resonant frequency at the start of heat exposure while the slower panting movements gradually accelerate with the increase in body temperature. Recordings of the movements caused by simultaneous panting and flutter in the cattle egret (*Bubulcus ibis*) are reproduced in fig. 4.9.

Finally, a feature which seems to be common to many panting animals, both bird and mammal, is that the respiratory response to really severe environmental conditions occurs in two phases. The first phase comprises the typical response of an increase in the frequency of breathing and a concurrent decrease in the depth of each breath. What has been called the 'second-phase breathing' is characterized by a secondary

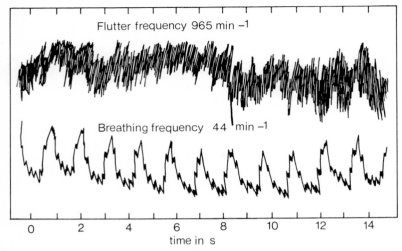

Fig. 4.9. Direct recordings of breathing movements (panting) and gular flutter in relation to time in the cattle egret (*Bubulcus ibis*) exposed to heat. (Based on work by Hudson *et al.* in Whittow, *Comparative Physiology of Thermoregulation*, Vol. I, 1970.)

decline from the maximal frequency and a secondary increase in the volume of air exchanged at each breath. By means of these changes the total ventilation during the second phase breathing is pushed to the maximum attainable, and maximum evaporation therefore also occurs at this time. The price for this is paid in the form of an increased oxygen consumption per unit of ventilation achieved.

4.2.4. *Heat Loss and Efficiency*

The trouble with panting as a means of dissipating excess body heat is that it may involve a considerable additional heat load on account of the extra activity of the respiratory muscles in increasing the ventilation. It still remains a matter of controversy as to whether the raised metabolism that is observed during panting is the result purely of the enhanced respiratory activity, or whether it is the direct result simply of the elevated body temperature. Whichever source may prove correct (and it may well be that both contribute) there is evidence that the heat tolerance of the dog, high as it is, may be limited by the 100 per cent increase in metabolism that occurs in severe panting. Recent experiments on the ox have shown, however, that the oxygen consumption attributable even to the more laboured second phase breathing is only about one-third of that during a similar increase in ventilation stimulated by breathing excess carbon dioxide instead of by external heat stress. If a similar economy obtains in the dog, the substantial increases measured in metabolic rate are still presumably of manageable proportions, for the dog exhibits as great a tolerance of heat as man enjoys by virtue of his sweat glands.

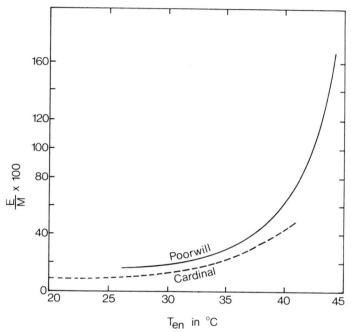

Fig. 4.10. A comparison of the efficiency of evaporative cooling (E) in two birds by panting (as seen in the cardinal, *Pyrrhuloxia cardinalis*) and by gular flutter (as in the poorwill, *Phalaenoptilus nuttallii*), expressed as a percentage of metabolic heat production. (Redrawn from Bartholomew, *Symp. Soc. Expl Biol.*, 1964.)

The position in birds is complicated by the occurrence of many different types of respiratory response to heat, but one important thing at least now appears to be established. This is that many birds, including both small and large species, are as successful as are mammals at evaporating all of their metabolic heat, even at ambient temperatures as high as 50°C. Once again there is some suggestion that species employing resonant panting or flutter are the more efficient in terms of maintaining thermal balance in severe conditions. Furthermore, the

91

extraordinary heat tolerance of a species such as the poorwill (*Phalae-noptilus nuttallis*) is no doubt in part due to the emphasis on resonant flutter of the gular pouch, which must consume far less oxygen than would the panting movements of the entire thorax (fig. 4.10).

The evaporative response of lizards to heat tends to take the form of a gradual rise in the frequency of breathing with increasing body temperature, presumably a less efficient respiratory reaction than that involving an abrupt change to a resonant frequency. Nevertheless, it does appear to have a significant cooling effect, so that species such as the desert iguana (*Dipsosaurus dorsalis*) are capable of maintaining body temperatures several degrees below that of a hot environment, and of evaporating a quantity of water equivalent to more than the heat production.

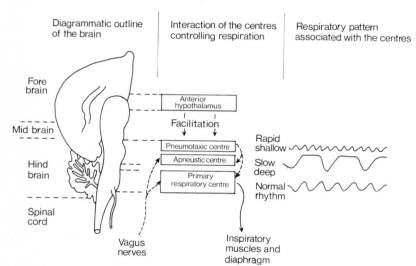

Fig. 4.11. A possible explanation of respiratory control in a panting mammal. Inspiration is the active phase of breathing, expiration being largely passive. Both the vagal and pneumotaxic mechanisms operate by inhibiting the inspiratory phase and thus decreasing the depth of breathing ; by allowing expiration to occur earlier than normal, they also accelerate the frequency. In panting, the hypothalamus appears to facilitate the action of either or both of these mechanisms.

4.2.5. *Regulation of Panting*

At this point, it is important that we should look briefly at the regulation of panting considered as a form of respiration. The neurones primarily responsible for governing the normal respiratory movements that mechanically ventilate the lungs at a rate finely adjusted to the body's requirements at a particular time, are found at various levels in the hind brain (fig. 4.11). Nearest to the spinal cord, the primary respiratory centre is capable of maintaining at least some form of rhythmic breathing even when isolated from all other parts of the brain. At somewhat higher levels there are two other groups of neurones of immediate importance. One (the apneustic centre) functions by reducing the breathing frequency set by the primary centre and by increasing the depth of each individual breath. The other (the pneumotaxic centre) has essentially the opposite characteristics in that it accelerates the frequency and reduces the depth. The function of this last centre is analogous to that of the vagus nerves in the neck. They connect the hind brain directly to receptors in the thorax, and section of the nerves in most animals is followed by a slowing and deepening of breathing ; this response is taken to imply that the normal function of the vagus nerves has the reverse effect. The importance of the accelerating influence of these two separate mechanisms, the vagal and the central, varies in different species. For instance, in the dog or the pigeon, the hind brain mechanism dominates to the extent that section of both vagus nerves has little effect on panting, whereas in the guinea pig or fowl, section of the nerves eliminates the ability to pant altogether.

We might summarize the present state of our understanding of how panting is controlled by saying that the hypothalamus appears to dominate the primary respiratory centres when evaporative cooling becomes necessary, in such a way that the enhanced ventilation that is required occurs by means of a rapid shallow form of breathing (rather than a slow deep form) which serves the cooling purpose and at the same time minimizes the undesirable side effects of over-ventilating the lungs.

4.2.6. *Secondary Effects of Panting*

Despite this emphasis on the rapid exchange of small breaths, there is still an increase, not only in the ventilation of the whole respiratory tract, but also in that of the lungs themselves. (This, presumably, is not the case where gular flutter is the sole response to heat stress.) As we have already seen, the effect of this is to wash out a greater proportion of the released carbon dioxide than is desirable, and this typically leads to an abnormally alkaline blood. Since one of the most important functions of the respiratory movements is the maintenance of a relatively constant balance between the alkaline and acidic factors in the blood, this consequence of over-ventilation is of great significance. It represents, in fact, the underlying basis of the conflict between the requirements of thermoregulation and those of acid-base equilibrium. Normally, a fall in blood carbon dioxide would result in a decline in total ventilation—even in extreme cases, by means of a complete cessation of breathing—so that the normal level would be allowed to build up in the lungs. In the heat, however, the panting animal often has no important means of evaporative cooling other than that provided by an increased respiratory ventilation, and the effect of this is further to exacerbate the acid-base imbalance. One of the peculiar adaptations of panting species appears to be their ability to tolerate considerably wider fluctuations in the direction of alkalinity than is the case with non-panting animals. Thus, in the dog, levels of blood carbon dioxide which in man would induce severe muscle cramps and even unconsciousness, are apparently withstood without any ill effects. Furthermore, there is recent evidence that the respiratory effects of reduced carbon dioxide may actually be reversed during heat stress, with the result that panting is further accelerated rather than depressed as we should expect.

These side effects would be very much greater were it not for the fact that a large proportion of the increased total ventilation which does occur during panting is restricted to the non-respiratory surfaces of the respiratory tract, and the lung itself is considerably protected. Indeed, during exposure to mild heat stress only, the diminished depth of breathing is sometimes sufficient to prevent any significant disturbances at all. But in severe conditions all panting species (apparently with the exception of the ostrich—see below) run into some degree of difficulty.

The source of the disturbances is clearly illustrated by experiments in which dogs are required to exercise either by running on a moving treadmill or by swimming in water. In the first case most of the heat generated has to be lost by evaporation from the respiratory tract, and there is, as a result, the usual reduction in blood carbon dioxide. Swimming, however, allows all of the heat produced to be dissipated by conduction to the water, with the result either that no change occurs in the blood carbon dioxide (in water at 30°C) or that the changes are actually in the opposite direction to those seen in the running and panting dog (in water at 15°C). In this second case, the metabolic heat is easily lost to the water and another side-effect is revealed, one that is usually obscured in the panting animal by the dominant respiratory effects. The exercising muscles build up an ' oxygen debt ' as soon as the rate at which oxygen is consumed is greater than that at which it can be supplied by the circulatory and respiratory systems. Muscle metabolism is then not fully aerobic and energy is liberated for the continued work by the anaerobic conversion of glycogen to lactic acid. This form of energy production is less efficient than full oxidation, but it does allow the muscles to continue functioning for the period of exercise while oxygen supplies are reduced. It is possible that this reduction of oxygen in the tissues is in some way related to the onset of the laboured second-phase breathing during exposure to severe heat stress.

The question of the secondary respiratory effects of panting has been studied a good deal in birds because the unique structural characteristics of the avian respiratory system were for long believed to provide for a large increase in total ventilation with maximum protection for the gas-exchange surfaces of the lungs. The reason for this was that the posterior air sacs in birds act as bellows by which the lungs may be ventilated, not as in mammals from a single opening (the trachea) in an otherwise closed bag, but both from the tracheal end and from the end

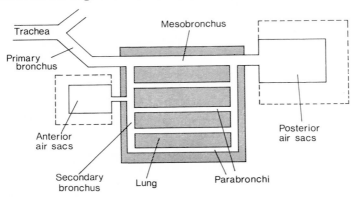

Fig. 4.12. Simplified diagram of the main structural characteristics of the respiratory system in birds.

connected directly to the posterior sacs (fig. 4.12). There are two potential pathways by which outside air could reach the bellows, a direct one involving no contact with the lung proper (through the mesobronchus), and an indirect one over the gas-exchange surface of the lung (through the parabronchi). The idea was that the opening into the indirect pathway could be reduced in diameter by contraction of the circular muscles at the entrance so that any increase in ventilation could be directed into the air sacs (where evaporation could occur) while the lung ventilation was unchanged.

While there is sound histological evidence for the existence of the necessary muscles, there is little from physiological studies on most birds to show that they operate effectively ; roughly the same order of changes in blood carbon dioxide occurs in the panting bird as in the mammal. The ostrich does appear to be a genuine exception and is, in fact, the only animal that has so far been shown capable of sustained panting in severe heat without suffering the expected consequences. This peculiarity may be related to the flightless existence of the ostrich. These giant birds encounter their maximum heat stress while quietly feeding or resting in the direct blaze of the sun rather than during a state of high metabolic activity. In such circumstances it may be necessary for them to increase the ventilation of the upper respiratory tract and air sacs only, while in flying birds an increased lung ventilation would also be needed to satisfy the concurrent need for more oxygen. It remains to be seen if this idea holds true for other flightless birds.

4.3. EVAPORATION FROM THE SKIN

The transfer of water through the cuticle of arthropods and the skin of amphibians and reptiles has often been measured, and has been shown to have biological significance (see Chapter 5). In these animals, however, any evaporative cooling which occurs is the passive and obligatory result of differences in vapour pressure, and there is seldom any suggestion of physiological control. Passive transfer of this kind occurs in homoiotherms as well, even in those forms which engage in active sweating at high environmental temperature, and the process often makes an important contribution to overall heat balance. Evaporative heat losses by passive and by active means are, however, best considered separately.

4.3.1. *Insensible Perspiration*

If an animal is exposed all day to a neutral environmental temperature it can be shown to lose a measurable quantity of its body mass. In man, this is commonly about 500 g. This loss is due to the transudation of moisture through the skin, and to the natural moistening of the air during breathing. The evaporation of this water at the surface of the skin and respiratory passages may account for the loss of a quarter of the total metabolic heat, and the term insensible perspiration is best reserved for this purely physical process, to distinguish it from the active secretion of fluid that occurs from the sweat glands and which is under a close physiological control. Non-sweating animals also lose significant amounts of water and heat by this means and, contrary to earlier opinion, it is now known that the cutaneous component may exceed that from the respiratory tract in some conditions.

There is a good deal of variation in the rate at which water is lost by insensible perspiration, and these differences are reflections of the varying physical factors which actually determine the vapour pressure gradients. The vapour pressure at the skin surface and in the air, together with the motion of the air, are the fundamental physical factors involved in determining the rate of water loss, and these are, of course, influenced by physiological factors such as skin temperature and the state of hydration of the skin. The physical nature of the process may be confirmed experimentally by showing that if the vapour pressure gradients are reversed, the skin is as capable of taking up atmospheric water as of losing it.

4.3.2. *Structure and Function of the Sweat Glands*

4.3.2.1. *Classification and terminology*

In the textbooks of mammalian or medical physiology you will find that sweat glands are divided into two groups, the eccrine and the apocrine. This time-honoured classification was introduced by P. Shiefferdecker in 1917, on the basis of histological studies with the light microscope, and on a postulated distinction between the methods of secretion of fluid by the two types which he derived from his structural evidence. The term eccrine (separated or secreted out of) described the discharge of fluid across the intact membrane of the glandular cell, without loss of cytoplasmic material or any change in appearance of the cell itself. Apocrine (secreted from), on the other hand, implied that a part at least of the secretion involved the rupture of the glandular cell wall, or the nipping off of tongue-like protuberances, and the discharge of this cytoplasmic material into the lumen of the gland. What Shiefferdecker also held, but what has been very largely ignored since his time, was that in his aprocrine glands the destructive or necrobiotic phase of secretion was followed by a phase during which a simple eccrine secretion was produced while the cells were regaining their initial form. Thus the fundamental distinguishing feature of the apocrine gland was its ability to engage in the so-called necrobiotic phase of secretion.

In the years since Shiefferdecker's publication there has been very extensive controversy on whether or not the apocrine glands do, in fact, employ this form of secretion ; so much so that the resulting confusion has led many authors to use the names eccrine and apocrine with reference only to the gross anatomical differences between the two types. Thus the difference in development in relation to the hair follicle, or minor differences in the mode of coiling or in the lining of the ducts, have been elevated to the status of fundamental distinguishing features, while at the same time the far more important functional characteristics that emerged from comparative studies have been passed over. What now seems clear is that the terms eccrine and apocrine should be used only to describe the two modes of secretion, the simple and the necrobiotic respectively. The mode of secretion is especially important in a consideration of the thermoregulatory role of the sweat glands for, as we shall see, it is almost certainly only the simple type of secretion that can have any functional significance in this connexion.

Accordingly, as a basic anatomical distinction, we shall adopt the recent suggestion of D. M. Jenkinson and J. Bligh and classify the sweat glands of various mammalian species as either ' atrichial ' (without hair) or ' epitrichial ' (upon the hair). That these terms are by no means synonyms for the eccrine and apocrine glands traditionally described will shortly become clear.

4.3.2.2. *Anatomy and distribution*

There is no need for us to spend a great deal of time in examining the detailed histology, still less the histochemistry, of the sweat glands, for we are concerned only with features of the glands which contribute to the regulation of body temperature. The chief anatomical characteristics of two representative glands are shown in fig. 4.13.

97

Typical atrichial glands occur on the foot-pads of several mammalian species, for instance the rat, dog and cat, although there is very little evidence that these have any thermoregulatory role. Otherwise, glands of this type are highly characteristic of the Anthropoidea, and have been described in the skin of several old-world monkeys, the chimpanzee, the

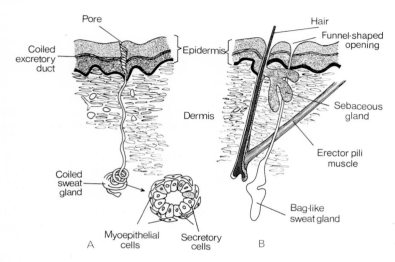

Fig. 4.13. The chief structural features of sweat glands known to function in temperature regulation. A. An atrichial gland of man with the secretory coil in cross-section. B. An epitrichial gland of the ox with its accompanying structures. The gland is similar in cross-section to the atrichial. (Based on Weiner and Hellman, *Biol. Rev.*, 1960 and Findlay and Yang, *J. agric. Sci.*, 1951.)

gorilla and others. By far the most marked development of atrichial glands is in man, where their density in different skin regions has been thoroughly investigated. It is highest on the palms and soles (200 mm^{-2}), moderate on the face (20–30 mm^{-2}) and least on the trunk and limbs (10–20 mm^{-2}); the total number may reach four millions in some individuals. The most important structural characteristic of these glands is that they develop directly from the epidermis and open on to the free surface of the skin. A significant histological feature (which, however, they share with the epitrichial glands) is the possession of longitudinally disposed smooth muscle fibres—the myoepithelium—between the secretory layer of cells and the basement membrane.

The epitrichial glands are far more characteristic of mammals as a whole, occurring in association with the hair follicles in most species so far examined. They vary a good deal in morphology and even more in

98

functional importance. Thus, while it has not been shown that the epitrichial glands in the dog and pig ever respond to the stimulus of heat, those of the ox have a considerable, and those of the horse a vital, importance in thermoregulation. The density of these glands, in so far as it is known, also varies considerably, from as high as 250 mm^{-2} on the neck of the ox and 100 mm^{-2} on its lower limbs, to an average of only about 25 mm^{-2} in the sheep. As their name implies, the epitrichial glands develop only in conjunction with the primary hair follicles ; they often open into the follicular canal, but in the cat, ox and pig may also open on to the free surface of the skin.

4.3.2.3. *The secretory process*

We have already mentioned that the sweat glands in different mammalian species differ greatly in the rate at which they produce secretions. They differ also, as Shiefferdecker knew, both in the nature of the secretory material and in the method by which it is produced. So far as thermoregulatory efficiency is concerned, it is desirable that the secreted substance should be a watery fluid that will evaporate readily from the surface of the skin, and that the rate of secretion should be geared to the particular heat-loss requirements at a given time. The first of these requirements seems to be met satisfactorily by the thermally-evoked secretions of all those mammals, such as man and horse, which depend on efficient sweating during heat exposure. Much less is known of the composition of the sweat of other animals, although the skin secretions of the sheep and ox certainly play a significant part in the overall heat balance of these species even though they employ panting also. We are not here concerned with the variety of secretions which manifestly do not contribute to thermoregulation.

The problem of the nature of the secretory process is more interesting. Although the atrichial glands that have been most studied are those of the cat's pad, there is every indication that these function in a way which is closely similar to the ones scattered over the entire human skin. The lumen of the gland fills with an aqueous fluid at a rate proportional to the frequency of impulses passing down the nerves supplying the gland. The impulses are believed to vary in frequency directly with the extent of elevation of the core body temperature above normal. Fluid emerges on to the surface of the skin only when the lumen of the gland is full, and since a certain amount of the fluid is reabsorbed in the duct of the gland, the rate at which it emerges is equal to the difference between the rates of secretion and reabsorption. This description fits the typical eccrine secretory process which has always been identified with the action of the thermal sweat glands of man. If you think of the process as a secretory pump which withdraws a watery fluid from the interstitial spaces of the skin, transfers it to the lumen of the gland, and pushes it on to the skin surface at a rate depending directly on the thermal state of the body, it will not be difficult to see how it can function as a thermoregulatory effector mechanism.

What is more difficult, indeed impossible, to see is how the necrobiotic secretory process, involving the actual breakdown and repair of the secretory cells, could be regulated as a heat-loss device, increasing and decreasing in rate with the state of thermal stress and the intensity of stimulation by either hormonal or nervous mechanisms. (As with all metabolic processes, the rate of even a necrobiotic secretion would be increased somewhat by a local rise in temperature.)

This is the major reason for abandoning the original Shiefferdecker classification. The so-called apocrine glands of the horse, donkey and llama, for example, are essential to the survival of these animals during exposure to heat or during exercise ; by implication, the glands must be secreting by some method other than the necrobiotic. Therefore, if we now recall Shiefferdecker's own belief that his apocrine glands employed a simple eccrine method in addition to the necrobiotic secretion, we begin to realize how it is that these non-primate mammals manage to achieve a high degree of thermal efficiency in the absence of atrichial sweat glands of the human variety. The epitrichial glands of many mammals have, in fact, developed an eccrine process of sweat secretion which appears to differ in no essential respect from that of the atrichial glands, and the arguments over the existence of a necrobiotic phase of secretion would seem to be wholly redundant so far as temperature regulation is concerned ; only a process that is amenable to central control of the rate of secretion of the glandular cells could possibly be effective. If we now examine the function of the sweat glands in a variety of species we shall see how the characteristic patterns are related to thermoregulatory effectiveness, and how the traditional classification based, as it is, solely on structural detail, has little to recommend it.

Let us take them in what is approximately an ascending order of thermal efficiency. First, the epitrichial glands of the pig, as already mentioned, have never been observed to discharge a fluid under any conditions of heat stress and their function remains largely unexplained. In the Welsh Mountain sheep and in some breeds of goat, a continuous discharge of sweat has also never been recorded, but instead there are intermittent discharges of moisture on to the skin which occur spontaneously and synchronously over the entire skin surface (fig. 4.14). Moreover, the frequency of the discharges has been shown to rise somewhat with increasing ambient temperature. The pattern of sweat discharge in these animals seems best explained as the result of a slow and uncontrolled secretion of the apocrine variety, the fluid being pushed out from the gland on to the skin at intervals by contraction of the myoepithelium. There is no marked increase in the rate of secretion with rising body temperature and the slight acceleration observed with increasing ambient temperature is probably the result of local increases in tissue metabolism. In view of the fact that the fluid is discharged on to the skin beneath the fleece it is in any case unlikely that this response bestows more than a minor thermoregulatory advantage. A few breeds of sheep and goats appear to show some general improvement on this pattern in that a relatively rapid discharge of sweat occurs (about once

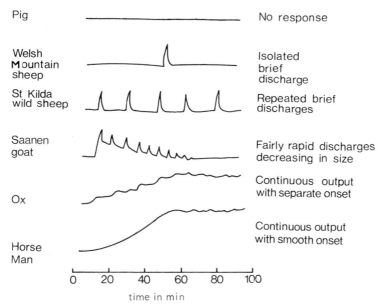

Fig. 4.14. Diagram of typical sweat gland activity in various mammalian species exposed to 40°C environmental temperature. (Based on work by Bligh, *Environl Res.*, 1967 and *Comp. Biochem. Physiol.*, 1969.)

every ten minutes), although the amount of moisture produced decreases with each successive discharge until after eight or nine any further myoepithelial contractions appear to be without effect. This is exactly what we should expect if the local heat-induced increases in myoepithelial contraction frequency were unaccompanied by sufficient increase in the rate of formation of fluid.

Sweating in cattle shows a considerable further advance in that the response to heat is a continuous secretion of moisture. There is, however, a marked stepwise onset to the sweating and also a regular occurrence of brief increments in the rate of secretion once the steady flow has been achieved (fig. 4.14). The most probable explanation of this pattern of sweat discharge is that the significant thermoregulatory component results from a simple eccrine secretion by the epitrichial glands, the rate of which increases with the degree of thermal stress. The periodic peaks in the outflow rate would then seem to be evidence of myoepithelial activity which has lost any thermoregulatory significance it might once have had, but which nevertheless still occurs.

In the horse and donkey there is a smooth onset of sweating in response to heat, very like that seen in man (fig. 4.14). In addition, there are sudden fluctuations in the rate of discharge in all these species which occur synchronously over widely different areas of the body. The explanation of these variations remains uncertain, since they differ in character from the sharp peaks seen in the ox and sheep. However, there seems every possibility that it is the same for the epitrichial glands of the horse and for the atrichial glands of man. While it is possible that in both species there may still remain vestiges of a nervously-controlled myoepithelial mechanism, the highly efficient thermal sweating itself is undoubtedly of the smooth, continuous, eccrine variety.

It is tempting to see in this series a sequence of steps in the evolution of an effective thermoregulatory system. While there may yet be insufficient evidence to justify any such conclusion, it remains distinctly possible that both the atrichial and epitrichial sweat glands of modern mammals have evolved from more primitive skin structures which performed some other function. The presence of myoepithelial cells in all known sweat glands, even in those which in no way depend on any contractile mechanism, may be evidence for the common origin of both types of gland. Equally, it may support the idea that the atrichial glands have arisen by modification from the more primitive epitrichial glands by losing the association with the hair follicle but by retaining and developing the eccrine secretory capability. In functional terms at least, there appears to be no essential difference between the secretory and discharge abilities of the epitrichial glands of cattle and horses on the one hand and the atrichial glands of man on the other.

4.3.2.4. *Innervation and regulation of secretory activity*

The sweat glands are connected to the hypothalamus by discrete nervous pathways through the sympathetic nervous system and spinal cord. The central and reflex control of sweating is a subject we shall consider in Chapter 6, and here we concentrate primarily on the nervous and hormonal mechanisms operating in the immediate vicinity of the glands themselves.

We still have very little knowledge of the anatomy of the terminal innervation of sweat glands. What information there is tends to conflict on the two possibilities that the glands either receive nerve endings which impinge directly on the secretory cells, or that their innnervation is based only on a general ground plexus without individual nerve endings. Whichever of these may prove to be the case—and there may well be specific differences—what we do know is that the various sweat glands fall into two categories depending upon the nature of the transmitter hormone which controls their function.

The distinction between the two types is based on the classical experiments of Sir Henry Dale (1875–1968) who more than forty years ago divided nerve fibres into two classes according to the substance that was liberated from the ends following stimulation. Nerves which liberated adrenaline (later shown to be the closely related noradrenaline) he termed adrenergic, and those yielding acetylcholine were called cholinergic. Working with W. Feldberg, Dale then investigated the innervation of the atrichial sweat glands of the cat's foot pad in terms of this fundamental distinction. After stimulating the sympathetic nerve chain, they were able to collect acetylcholine but not noradrenaline in the fluid perfusing the intact pad, but no acetylcholine was collected when the tissue of the pad that actually contained the sweat glands was tied off. This was a surprising result, for one of the distinguishing characteristics of the sympathetic division of the autonomic nervous system is that its nerve endings liberate noradrenaline, whereas those of the parasympathetic system give off acetylcholine. The cat's atrichial glands were thus innervated by nerves that were sympathetic in origin yet cholinergic in function. The same is now known to be true of the atrichial glands in man.

This was such an important discovery that it is worth pausing for a moment to consider the evidence by which it may be confirmed. The most important is as follows : (i) subcutaneous injection of a drug called pilocarpine, which stimulates the parasympathetic nervous system, also induces profuse sweating ; (ii) administration of another drug, atropine, which blocks the action of acetylcholine, suppresses normal sweating and antagonizes the effect of pilocarpine ; (iii) histochemical staining techniques have shown that the enzyme cholinesterase, which splits acetylcholine, occurs in the neighbourhood of the sweat glands ; the presence of cholinesterase is considered characteristic of cholinergic fibres, its function being to prevent unduly prolonged action of the acetylcholine when it is released ; (iv) monoamine oxidase, the equivalent enzyme found near adrenergic fibres, is not present ; (v) injection of noradrenaline directly into the blood stream does not elicit sweating, while that of acetylcholine does. (Sweating induced by intradermal noradrenaline injections in man has been described, but any minor adrenergic component that there might be in the innervation of the atrichial glands has never been shown to play any part in thermally-induced sweating.)

By contrast with the thermal sweat glands of man, it is known that the normal physiological control of the glands in the horse and ox is exerted by adrenergic mechanisms. However, in the horse at least, it seems that sweating results, not from the liberation of hormones at the nerve endings, but from the presence of adequate levels of blood-borne adrenaline released from the adrenal glands. Direct stimulation of the sympathetic nerve chain in the horse inhibits sweating, but the adrenergic nature of the control is confirmed by the presence of mono-amine oxidase and the absence of cholinesterase in the horse's sweat glands. Similar mechanisms may operate in the sheep, goat and donkey, but it seems that the primary response in these species is mediated by adrenergic nerves.

4.3.2.5. *Sweating rate and sweat gland fatigue*

The simplest and commonest method for the quantitative assessment of the rate of sweating is that of accurate weighing of the subject before, during and after an experiment. A correction is made for losses of moisture from the respiratory tract and, of course, for any lost as urine and faeces. In recent years this approach has been supplemented by the use of a ventilated capsule technique which relies in principle on measuring the change in humidity of air passing at a known rate over a known area of skin enclosed within a capsule which itself is sealed to the shaved skin. The rate of uptake of water vapour by the air stream is taken as the rate of water loss from the skin. In studies involving also the analysis of the chemical composition of the sweat, actual collection may be performed by enclosing a sweating appendage in a waterproof bag or by washing down the subject or animal with a measured quantity of distilled water.

The amount of sweat secreted is regulated so as to match the thermoregulatory requirements of the body. Rates of sweating within a species differ widely, however, with a number of factors, including individual variation, age, sex, skin area, degree of adaptation to the hot conditions, and period of exposure. The great majority of quantitative studies have been carried out on young men, at rest and naked, where, in still air, sweating generally begins at an environmental temperature of about 31°C. As a result of the sweating mechanism extremely high temperatures, far above those occurring in nature, can be tolerated for short periods, provided that the air is dry and evaporation rapid. The most dramatic demonstration of this was described by C. Blagden in 1775. Two men entered a chamber at 127°C, taking with them an uncooked beef steak. After some twenty minutes, during which time the men maintained tolerable body temperatures by evaporating moisture at a furious rate (as may be confirmed, under essentially similar conditions, in a sauna bath), the beef steak was said to be cooked. In marked contrast to this is the situation in which evaporation is impeded by very high humidity ; heat stroke and even deaths have been recorded in man at ambient temperatures as low as 32°C when at rest, or at 22°C during sustained and strenuous exercise.

So far as the actual rate of sweating is concerned, many workers have measured in man discharges in excess of 2 litres per hour during exposure to high temperatures. The rate varies widely with work load (fig. 4.15). The equivalent of 4 l h⁻¹ is claimed for well-adapted man, although such activity can obviously be maintained only for short periods. The maximum recorded over a 24-hour period in hot, dry conditions at Boulder City, Nevada is 12 litres, equivalent to more than 29 000 kJ of heat (evaporation of 1 litre of moisture releases about 2450 kJ).

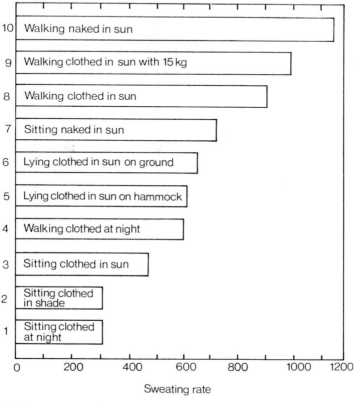

Fig. 4.15. Average sweating rates (expressed as rate of loss of water in gram per hour) under various conditions of exposure in the desert, all at air temperatures of 38°C. (After Gosselin in Adolph, *Physiology of Man in the Desert*, 1947.)

When very high rates of sweating (1·0–1·5 l h⁻¹) are stimulated by sustained exposure to heat, fatigue of the sweat glands occurs irrespective of the state of dehydration, of salt loss or degree of adaptation to the conditions. The site of the fatigue is generally considered to be the

H   105

secretory cells themselves, and this must be the case in the horse where sweating is not activated by nervous stimulation. The condition called dry-coat, as described in horses imported into hot, wet climates (such as in Malaya) from the temperate zone, has been thoroughly investigated. The failure to sweat is preceded by a period of profuse sweating, caused by high levels of adrenaline in the blood and brought about by the environmental heat stress, often exacerbated by exercise. Ultimately, the sweat glands accommodate to the raised adrenaline and thus become insensitive to it. Affected horses suffer profound hyperthermia on exercise and there have been many deaths on the race course. The vicious circle of dry-coat can be broken only by rest in a cooler climate. A completely normal sweating response may then be re-established, only to fail again on a second exposure to the humid heat.

4.3.2.6. *The efficiency of sweating and the role of humidity*

The value of sweating as a thermoregulatory effector depends on the ability of the moisture secreted to evaporate. In a hot dry atmosphere evaporative cooling is highly efficient, whereas in humid heat sweating may be grossly inefficient because up to two-thirds of the sweat secreted may run off the skin without being evaporated. (Paradoxically, even this apparent wastage may play a useful physiological role by washing away salt which otherwise accumulates on the skin and lowers the vapour pressure to a degree which in humid conditions can be significant.) In general, we might assess the physiological efficiency of sweating in terms of the evaporative cooling of the skin relative to the specific latent heat of the sweat produced :

$$\text{Sweating efficiency} = \frac{\text{Heat removed by evaporation}}{\text{Total specific latent heat of moisture secreted}} \times 100$$

The effect of humidity on evaporative cooling from the skin of naked, resting man is insignificant at air temperatures up to about 25°C, because a sufficient vapour pressure gradient can always be established between the skin and the air. For example, at a room temperature and humidity of 20°C and 80 per cent r.h. the vapour pressure on the skin (average temperature 33°C) would be about 5 kPa compared to that in the air of 2 kPa. At above about 30°C, however, humidity begins to assume great importance. A simple vapour pressure gradient is no longer sufficient to ensure adequate evaporation, and heat balance is achieved only by a physiological variation in the area of wetness of the skin, which compensates for the falling gradient. The concept of the relative humidity of the skin (which is analogous to the relative humidity of the air) is often used in preference to the area of wetness. It is the ratio of the vapour pressure on the surface of the skin to that of the air when saturated at skin temperature, and represents an estimate of the water content of the skin as a percentage of the maximum value when the entire skin surface is covered with water. The variations observed in the relative humidity of the skin are quite simple to understand, because they occur just as if the passage of water through the skin were a simple process of diffusion governed by the rate at which the water is taken up by the environment. For instance, a rise in the humidity of the environment would lead to a fall in water loss from the skin surface ; however, tissue fluid continues to diffuse through the skin and this would raise the skin humidity so that the rate of evaporation again comes to equal the rate of upward diffusion. The temperature of the skin also plays a facilitating role in that decreased evaporation causes it to rise, thus widening the thermal gradient from skin to air, and accelerating evaporation by this means.

In this connexion, however, we must remember that the drop in skin temperature which occurs as a result of evaporation increases the thermal gradient from core to surface and therefore reduces the volume of blood flowing to the skin, and with it the amount of body heat that would otherwise have been carried. In a similar way, the lowered skin temperature may also have adverse effects on heat balance by increasing the direct flow of heat to the body surface during exposure to high ambient temperature. The rate of evaporation has to be regulated so as to overcome these two disadvantages.

4.3.2.7. *Secondary effects of sweating*

The only constituents of sweat that have special importance in thermal physiology are the water and the salt. Human sweat, the only type for which there is much information, is more than 99 per cent water, but normally contains from 2 to 4 g of sodium chloride per litre as well as insignificant amounts of other ions. The average daily European diet contains about 10 g of common salt, which is greatly in excess of that normally used, as is shown by the fact that most of it is excreted. However, exposure to tropical heat, especially if it is accompanied by hard physical work, can lead to the loss of over 30 g of salt per day. Even less severe conditions can easily lead to a salt deficit, especially if, as often happens, the water losses are replaced by drinking without thought to the replacement of salt. The first symptom of salt deficiency is painful cramps in the muscles (stoker's cramp), a situation which can be avoided by taking excess salt in the diet or cured by drinking appropriate quantities of 0·5 per cent saline. The success of the 8th Army in the desert campaigns of the Second World War was partly the result of their being given to drink a salt solution closely similar in composition to sweat. Somewhat more appealing, and hardly less effective, was the traditional haymaker's remedy ; this merely required the consumption of copious amounts of beer or cider, which roughly restore the salts where water or tea do not.

If preventive steps of one sort or another are not taken, a vicious cycle may be established with really serious consequences. Thus the loss of salt affects mostly the extracellular fluid (that is, largely the blood plasma and the tissue fluid lying between the cells), which then loses water to the cells as a result of its reduced osmotic pressure. The intracellular fluid therefore increases in volume. The lowered osmolarity causes the kidney to re-absorb less water in the renal tubules, and this is followed by a further drop in extracellular fluid volume. There is now a loss of appetite which reduces the salt intake, and the progressive depletion causes vomiting and diarrhoea and thus still further loss of salt from the body.

The electrolyte imbalance caused by salt depletion most often occurs, then, when body water is being satisfactorily maintained by drinking. On the other hand, when water is not available to replace that lost in sweat, dehydration follows, and if severe this would ultimately lead to failure of the thermoregulatory system, an explosive rise in body temperature and death from hyperthermia.

One of the special problems for man in dehydration is that water is lost from the blood plasma at a rate that is usually more than twice as rapid as that by which it is lost from the body as a whole. For instance, a level of dehydration amounting to 4 per cent of the body mass is accompanied by a plasma reduction of 10 per cent. This is particularly unfortunate because during heat stress the circulatory system is already under special strain as a result of the maximal cutaneous vasodilatation. With the fall in plasma volume there is an increase in the blood viscosity and consequently an increased strain on the pumping mechanism of the heart. There is insufficient blood to supply the sweat glands with water, and insufficient effectively to transfer heat from the interior of the body to the skin. This leads to a general instability of the circulation, with reduced blood pressure, and giddiness or fainting because of the poor supply to the brain.

Prolonged and profuse sweating in man is invariably accompanied by a degree of dehydration of the order of 2 to 4 per cent, even when abundant water is available. Under these conditions the increase in osmotic pressure and decrease in blood volume stimulate the kidney to reabsorb more water and reduce the output of urine by as much as 80 per cent. The underlying reason for man's so-called voluntary dehydration seems to be that his drinking capacity, even that of the most thirsty student, is much smaller than in many other mammals, and normally limited to about one litre per hour. This, of course, is related to the loss of desire to drink which occurs before the evaporated water has been replaced.

The donkey handles its water balance problems much more effectively than man ; it regains any water lost in sweat rapidly and precisely, drinking if necessary at rates up to almost 10 litres per minute. Another advantage possessed by the donkey and by the camel is that, for reasons still largely unknown, water is lost not from the plasma but from the general body water stores outside the vascular system. In the camel up to 30 per cent of the body mass can be lost by evaporation of water before any change occurs in the circulation or in the mechanisms of heat loss. In addition, this vast quantity of water (more than 150 litres) can be replaced during a single drinking session. The performance of various animals in tolerating extremes of environmental heat is considered further in Chapter 7.

CHAPTER 5
behavioural thermoregulation

WE should be surprised if animals did not react to temperature at all. Indeed, we are often first aware of their temperature responses when we observe their attempts to occupy favourable thermal conditions. Even in our own case, we commonly respond to the stimulus of heat or cold by *doing* something, by opening the windows or by putting on a coat. Man's success in inhabiting the whole range of the earth's climatic conditions is in fact attributable more to his behaviour than to any special physiological performance. He may live happily at the South Pole by providing for himself a protected climate within his clothing or his heated buildings, by which he actually avoids the polar conditions, or he may reside with complete comfort in the humid tropics by providing his dwellings with artificial ventilation or even full air-conditioning. Although animals obviously lack man's technological skills, they share with him this ability to seek out or to create protected niches within a hostile climatic zone, such that their physiology may differ in no way from that of related species living in more temperate regions. Nest-building may greatly enhance the insulation available to an arctic animal, while burrowing or nocturnal behaviour make the hottest deserts inhabitable even by small rodents.

Generally speaking, an animal in the wild compensates for fluctuations in its thermal environment simply by moving to a warmer or cooler place. Locomotor responses of this kind have been investigated in practically all types of animal, and they are no less important in the minority of creatures that can also regulate body temperature by physiological means than they are in the majority which possess little or no such ability. While physiological conformity is often thought of as the opposite of regulation, metabolic compensations for temperature are of such major importance in the lives of many poikilothermic animals that we shall have to consider some aspects in Chapter 7. For the present, however, it will be convenient to distinguish the metabolic effects of temperature from the behavioural effects which, at least by implication, must involve some form of intervention by the nervous system.

Here we immediately run into difficulties. It is the organism as a whole that responds to the thermal environment, and it is of the utmost importance that we should see the separation of these responses into behaviour and physiology as nothing more than an arbitrary device of

110

convenience to biologists. This is what was meant in Chapter 1 in relation to Martin's fine physiological study of the development of homoiothermy. By the same token, if we took a frog or a lizard into the laboratory and investigated its temperature relations in a closed and artificial situation, we might be fortunate enough to discover some interesting facts about its physiological potentialities, but if we isolated these in our minds from the ecology and behaviour of the animal we should be dealing with little more than a biological artifact. Our experiments would very likely indicate that the creature is a defenceless poikilotherm, entirely at the mercy of its ambient temperature, yet the same animal interacting with the multiple thermal parameters of its natural environment may be a highly versatile ectotherm with remarkable regulating ability.

Throughout the present chapter then, we shall be mainly concerned, as a matter of convenience, with the whole-body responses of animals which contribute towards tolerance of the thermal environment. There will be some instances where these responses may appear to be more physiological than behavioural, and still others where any such distinction would be impossible to make. Debate on such issues is seldom profitable, for it tends only to harden the artificial barriers of traditional biology when so much of our contemporary science tells us that we should strive to bring them down. In dealing with the various groups of poikilothermic animals we will begin with what may be called the descriptive approach of the natural historian and go on, where the information is available, to the experimental approach of the comparative physiologist, who investigates the mechanisms underlying the behaviour. With the homoiotherms this is more difficult, and we shall be forced to employ yet further arbitrary divisions and to leave most of the discussion of physiological mechanisms to Chapter 6.

5.1. TEMPERATURE RESPONSES OF POIKILOTHERMS

5.1.1. *Invertebrates*

Far more is known about the temperature relations of terrestrial arthropods, notably insects, than about those of any other invertebrates. It is among certain of these creatures that the behavioural mechanisms of temperature regulation not uncommonly result in body temperatures many degrees higher than air temperature. In some cases they are as high as those normally associated with endotherms.

Many insect species have been shown capable of selecting a preferred or optimum range of temperature when placed in a continuous gradient, and such locomotor or orientation mechanisms are typically adapted to the biology of the species. For instance, the preferred temperature of the free-ranging cockroach *Blatta orientalis* is 20–29°C, while that of

111

the human louse (*Pediculus humanus corporis*) is restricted to 29–30°C, the usual temperature between the clothes and skin.

Some insects do not rely solely on air temperature as the means of adjusting the temperature of their bodies, but use in addition direct heat from the sun's rays. This implies a more sophisticated temperature-sensing system, which is indicated both by gross movements in and out of the sunlight and by fine movements designed to expose a variable surface area. Several species of locusts expose a maximum surface by orienting their bodies so that the longitudinal axis is at right angles to the sun's rays when the air is cool in morning and evening, but then adopt a position parallel to the rays during the heat of the day. Basking behaviour of this variety may yield a body temperature up to 15 K above that of the air and greatly accelerates the attainment of the temperature necessary for flight.

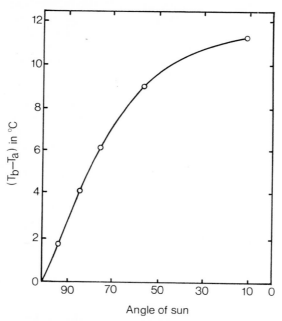

Fig. 5.1. The excess of body temperature over an air temperature of 17·5°C in the butterfly *Boloria chariclea* as affected by the angle of incidence of the sun's rays to the wings. (Redrawn from Keven and Shorthouse, *Arctic*, 1970.)

Several butterflies found in arctic Canada appear to be wholly dependent upon basking activity, and therefore on the heat of the sun, in order to maintain sufficient activity for survival. They regulate the rate of heat gain by varying the area of wing surface exposed to the sun and by raising or lowering the anterior parts of the body so as to change the angle of its transverse axis to the sun's rays. The latter response is remarkably effective in increasing the excess of body temperature over ambient temperature (fig. 5.1). Furthermore, the selection of bare ground as resting places in preference to vegetation some distance from the ground enhances warming by reflected radiation and attenuates the cooling rates of the butterflies during cloudy weather.

Extreme heat is commonly avoided in many invertebrates by means of burrowing activity. If they are exposed to the air, passive evaporative water loss occurs at a rate which is dependent largely upon the nature of the animal's integument. Although this often results in a reduction of body temperature, the device is of limited value since desiccation probably kills more ectotherms than does heat itself. In several species of woodlice, E. B. Edney showed that the reduction in temperature caused by evaporation was identical in living and dead specimens, thus confirming that water loss is not under physiological control. However, in *Blatta orientalis* up to 13 per cent of the body mass can be lost per hour by evaporation, and since the difference between body temperature and environmental temperature widens as the latter rises this could, in effect, have some limited thermoregulatory value.

The desert cicada (*Diceroprocta apache*) is constantly faced with potentially lethal temperatures in its Arizona habitat, and it has responded to this not only by the development of exceptional heat tolerance but also by behaviour which increases the loss of heat and inhibits its gain. The insect is thus able to remain active during the hottest part of the day, when its predators have retreated to shelter. Having first achieved its preferred body temperature of 35–39°C soon after sunrise by means of basking and orientation movements, the cicada moves to north-facing perches, which minimize further exposure. By this simple expedient body temperature may then be maintained several degrees below that of the air. The insects are strong fliers, and so long as the body temperature is below about 39°C they make extended flights. In the course of this activity the body temperature may rise by up to 8 K and a further behavioural adaptation is seen in the fact that at high environmental temperatures flights are restricted to between 1 and 3 seconds. Body temperature can then be kept below the critical level of 45·6°C at which motor control is lost.

Many butterflies and moths attain high body temperatures prior to flight as a result of their own metabolic (endothermic) heat production. This is achieved by shivering movements of the flight muscles. During the warm-up period, muscles that are normally antagonists in flight contract synchronously. As the body (chiefly the thorax) warms, the muscles contract more rapidly and powerfully until, at the temperature for flight, the contractions shift abruptly to the alternating pattern which flaps the wings. The time required to warm up to the minimum temperature for flight is inversely related to ambient temperature, and during flying activity the muscle temperature of many of these insects reaches more than 35°C, which may easily be 20 K above that of the air. In the sphinx moth *Celeria lineata* strong flight is possible at 25°C body temperature, but the moth does not take to the air voluntarily below 32°C, by which time muscular activity is reaching peak efficiency. Body temperature is controlled during activity with extraordinary accuracy by a combination of shivering, short bursts of flight and a variety of behavioural reactions which accelerate cooling and minimize heat gain (fig. 5.2). It seems, in fact, that some large endothermic insects (the sphinx moth is 45 mm long) possess a freedom from environmental temperature that is comparable to that of many of the small birds and mammals, which must resort to energy-conserving behaviour such as periodic torpor (see Section 5.21) when the cost of homoiothermy is too great.

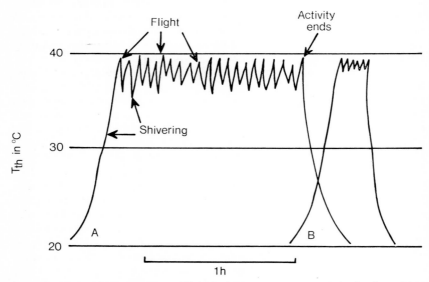

Fig. 5.2. Thoracic temperature (T_{th}) during spontaneous activity in the sphinx moth *Celeria lineata*. A. The temperature increases from ambient (20–22°C) as a result of shivering and is kept within a narrow range during a sequence of short flights, cooling and re-heating by shivering. B. A period of continuous flight following shivering. (Based on work by Adams and Heath, *Nature*, 1964.)

Another species of sphinx moth, *Manduca sexta*, has been shown to adjust the rate of its heat loss by circulatory changes at times when heat production cannot be regulated. *M. sexta* is nocturnal, and must perform sustained hovering flight while feeding on nectar. Hovering is only possible when the thoracic temperature reaches 38°C, and this is attained by shivering. During periods of low ambient temperature the heat generated is lost to the air by radiation and convection, but in high ambient temperatures the heat loss is accelerated by increasing the rate of circulation of the haemolymph (blood). Heat generated in the thorax is transferred to the blood pumped from the dorsal vessel and is dissipated when the blood returns to the abdomen, where the temperature is only slightly above ambient. Variations of this mechanism allow the maintenance of a nearly stable thoracic temperature during flight in a wide range of ambient conditions.

Individuals of the honeybee (*Apis mellifera*), when outside the hive, have a considerable ability to regulate their body temperatures during the day by means of altering the rate of heat production. In moderately warm weather they maintain a temperature of 35–36°C, accelerating the metabolic rate and consuming more food as soon as ambient temperature falls. According to A. Heusner and T. Stussi the metabolism of a bee under these conditions is comparable to that of a homoiotherm, if allowance is made for the differences of size and body temperature. At night, however, or during cold weather, the bee is strictly ectothermic and heat production varies directly with temperature.

Metabolic heat is used in social insects such as bees and hornets to maintain a relatively constant temperature in the nest or hive. Thus the honeybee hive as a whole behaves rather differently from the individual bees, regulating its temperature within quite a narrow range at both high and low ambient temperatures. In cold weather the bees gather closely together, thus reducing the exposed surface area, and the core of the cluster remains at a comparatively constant temperature. Below about 5°C ambient temperature the cluster core temperature actually increases as the environment cools and decreases as it warms up as a result of marked changes in the rate of heat production. When ambient temperature rises, the cluster expands as the bees move further apart, and the heat production falls. In addition, individual bees transport water to the hive and deposit it on the combs. Beating movements of the wings are then used to drive a current of air over the moisture. The air is cooled by evaporation, and hive temperature can be maintained at 38°C in an ambient temperature of 50°C. With such behaviour, it is hardly surprising that the thermoregulation seen in a beehive is sometimes compared to that of a homoiothermic animal.

Entirely different problems are faced by aquatic invertebrates, since they cannot use evaporative cooling and therefore cannot have body temperatures lower than water temperature. Their heat exchange is dominated by physical considerations, and there is little or no possibility of thermoregulation. Semi-aquatic species, such as inter-tidal barnacles and limpets, do lose body heat by evaporation, although it is only in species such as the fiddler crab (*Uca pugnax*) that behavioural responses

115

appear to influence this passive transpiration. The crabs are commonly found on sand as hot as 50°C, but maintain a tolerable body temperature by periodically returning to their burrows, which are a good deal cooler. Furthermore, there is evidence of a circadian rhythm of light-sensitivity, whereby the crabs are attracted to light (and warmth) in the early morning but are repelled by them during the hottest part of the day.

Our knowledge of the mechanisms underlying behavioural responses of invertebrates is extremely limited, and restricted almost entirely to insects. Sensitivity to high temperatures seems to be a property of the entire body surface, although the antennae may contain special thermal sense organs in some species. One of the few insects in which we have evidence from electrophysiological techniques is the cockroach *Periplaneta americana*. The antennae possess special organs which are sensitive to cold, or at least to rapidly falling ambient temperature. The discharge of electrical impulses from the sense organs increases as the temperature is lowered, and decreases as it is raised. However, in each case, the discharge frequency soon returns to the original level. There are also thermal receptors between the claws and on the tarsal segments, which appear to discharge impulses chiefly at temperatures both higher and lower than that to which the animal is accustomed (fig. 5.3).

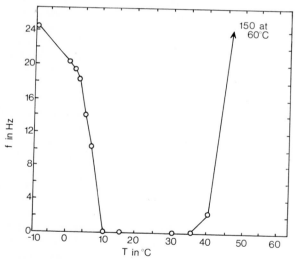

Fig. 5.3. Frequency of electrical impulses (*f*) from tarsal receptors of *Periplaneta americana* in relation to temperature. The impulses were recorded from the tibial nerve of a cockroach accustomed to 22°C and then subjected to various temperature changes. (Redrawn and modified from G. A. Kerkut and B. J. Taylor, *J. exptl Biol.*, **34**, 1957.)

5.1.2. *Fishes*

As with aquatic invertebrates, most fish have body temperatures virtually indistinguishable from that of the water. This is a direct consequence of the fact that even saturated water contains only about 5 per cent of the oxygen that occurs in the same volume of air, so that large quantities must be allowed to flow past the gills to ensure adequate supplies of oxygen to the tissues. In the process, water and blood come to the same temperature. Of course, physiological compensation does occur in fish such that the metabolic rate of individuals of a species. found at 5 °C may be as high as that of other individuals found at 10 °C, but this is an adaptation quite different from that of temperature regulation.

The chief means of behavioural temperature regulation available to fish is that of selecting in a thermal gradient the temperature that is best suited to the particular physiological capabilities of the species. This is presumed to be a major factor explaining the distribution of fish in nature.

Two groups of fish, however, have developed a substantial independence of water temperature by their ability to conserve metabolic heat and to control the efficiency of this conservation. These are the tunnies (sub-order Scombroidei) and the lamnid sharks (sub-order Galeoidei), species in which rapid sustained swimming is an essential part of their predatory habits. In most fish the blood is supplied to the active musculature from a centrally-positioned dorsal aorta passing just beneath the vertebrae, with segmental arteries running outwards towards the periphery. In the tunnies and lamnid sharks the situation is quite different ; the major arteries and veins are located just beneath the skin at the sides of the body and the smaller vessels pass inward towards the vertebrae. What is more, the entire system is composed of parallel arteries and veins in close contact. The vessels passing to and from the dark red muscle that is responsible for sustained swimming movements break up into complex retia which act as highly efficient counter-current heat exchangers. The considerable quantity of heat generated in the powerful muscles is thus conserved by transfer to the veins, and becomes available for warming the tissues of the fish by several degrees, instead of being merely lost at the gills. When we realize that water has a specific heat capacity some 3000 times as great as air, and that thermal diffusion is about 10 times as rapid as the diffusion of molecules of oxygen, we can see what a remarkable system of metabolic heat retention these fishes have developed.

We already know that warm muscle is more powerful than cold (see also below) and can therefore imagine the contribution that this heat-exchanger makes in the extraordinary swimming feats recorded for individual blue-fin tunny (*Thunnus thynnus*). These fish have been known to swim from the region of the Bahamas, where water temperature is about 30°C, to near Norway at 6°C, a distance of 4200 miles,

117

in less than fifty days. They are apparently quite independent of these water temperatures, and do, in fact, regulate the temperature of their muscle mass so that it varies by little more than 5 K over this ambient range. Exactly how this is achieved is not yet clear, but there must be a substantial modification in the heat-exchanger efficiency which is under the fish's control. Other species of tunny, notably the skipjack (*Katsuwonus pelamis*) and yellowfin (*Thunnus albacares*), do not migrate over great distances, but spend most of their lives in water at about 20°C. They are capable of maintaining their muscle temperatures consistently above water temperature, but they do not appear to thermoregulate nearly so well as the bluefin (fig. 5.4).

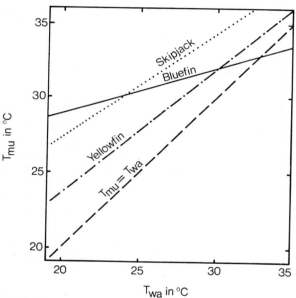

Fig. 5.4. Muscle temperature (T_{mu}) of three species of tuna in relation to water temperature. See text. (Redrawn from Carey and Teal, *Comp. Biochem. Physiol.*, 1969.)

The adaptations to the vascular system seen also in the lamnid sharks fit them equally well for their way of life ; the similarities between such widely separated groups of fish thus seem to be well explained in terms of their mutual need for high-speed swimming, a need that is met far more readily by warm muscle than by cold. (For a 10 K rise in temperature a muscle generally contracts about three times as fast with no loss of contractile force. The power generated is thus three times as great.) The physiology of the two groups has been beautifully adapted to their behavioural requirements.

118

Attempts to understand the mechanisms underlying the performance of fishes in sensing small differences in temperature have increased in recent years, although we still have only scanty data. More than ten years ago it was shown, rather dramatically, that goldfish could be trained to actuate a valve in their aquarium which introduced a small amount of cold water to counteract an otherwise steadily rising water temperature. The fish proved able to maintain their water at between 33·5 and 36·5°C for most of the time, a performance which, it was noted, was roughly equal in precision to that of rats in an analogous situation. The site for the reception of changes in temperature is usually said to be nerve endings scattered all over the skin, although in sharks there is some evidence that the ampullae of Lorenzini are organs of temperature (and pressure) reception.

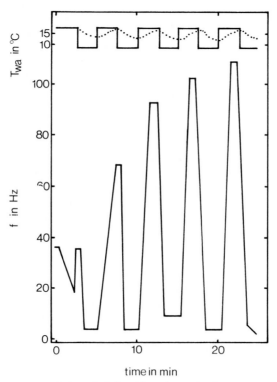

Fig. 5.5. Frequency of electrical impulses in a single warm-sensitive neuron during repeated cycles of warming and cooling the brain of the brook trout (*Salvelinus fontinalis*). An estimate of brain temperature is shown by the dotted line. (Based on work by Greer and Gardner, *Science*, **169**, pp. 1220–1222, 18 September 1970 Copyright 1970 by the American Association for the Advancement of Science.)

119

The probability that thermal sensitivity resides in the brain itself, as well as over the body surface, has been shown in recent experiments where the brains of various species have been heated or cooled artificially. This is achieved either by perfusing the gills with warm or cool water or, more delicately, by implanting small U-shaped metal tubes (thermodes) into selected areas of the brain and passing water through the tubes from a pump. Thus arctic sculpins of the genus *Myoxocephalus*, which were adapted to water at 5°C, would escape from water at substantially higher temperature as soon as their deep body temperatures had risen from 5°C to about 8°C. The time spent in the warm water was shortened by warming the forebrain, and this procedure also reduced the rise in core temperature before escape occurred. Conversely, cooling the forebrain caused an increase in the body temperature, and sometimes suppressed altogether the escape from the warm water.

Direct recordings of action potentials from single neurons within the brain of the American brook trout (*Salvelinus fontinalis*) have yielded further impressive evidence for the central detection of changes in temperature. Warming the brain would elicit activity from some neurons (fig. 5.5), while cooling it elicited activity from others, just as occurs in the mammalian brain (Chapter 6). Indeed, the striking thing about these behavioural and neuronal responses is that they so closely resemble those seen in mammals in similar circumstances. Once again they show that, provided the ectothermic animal is not deprived of its normal behavioural responses, it is often far more adept at maintaining a relatively constant body temperature than has been traditionally believed. While we are still in the early days of exploration so far as fish and all non-mammalian vertebrates are concerned, it seems highly likely that the origins of the central thermostat which was thought to be so characteristic of the endotherms, is detectable in ectothermic forms which utilize its thermal sensitivity primarily to activate behavioural responses.

5.1.3. *Amphibians*

Rather less is known about thermoregulation in amphibians than in fish. This is a pity, because as a group they are of great zoological interest, bridging the gap between those types of animal organization that are entirely aquatic and those that are entirely terrestrial.

Water moves relatively freely in either direction through amphibian skin, and it is this feature which puts the greatest single restriction on the animals' movements. Evaporation of water may be of value in some circumstances, but since the skin must be kept moist for respiratory purposes, frequent access to water is imperative for the great majority of species. The aquatic salamanders and many larval forms depend on habitat selection, while many of the more terrestrial amphibians take advantage of their low metabolic rates by remaining dormant for long periods, emerging only when conditions are favourable. Many frogs and toads are nocturnal, using the higher humidities and lower temperatures of the night to avoid the danger of desiccation, although some forms do bask in the sun, when they may attain body temperatures of 10 K or more above air temperature. Naturally, such basking is combined with shade-seeking behaviour if temperatures get dangerously high.

In emergency, many amphibians resort to evaporative cooling to postpone lethal body temperatures. The frog *Rana pipiens* can maintain a body temperature of 35°C for up to three hours in air temperatures of 50°C, while the Australian tree frog (*Hyla rubella*) survives for eight hours or more at 40°C. It is interesting that a closely related species, *Hyla coerulea*, survives the stress of radiant heat much better when intact than when pithed, suggesting some form of central nervous control rather than the mere passive transpiration of water.

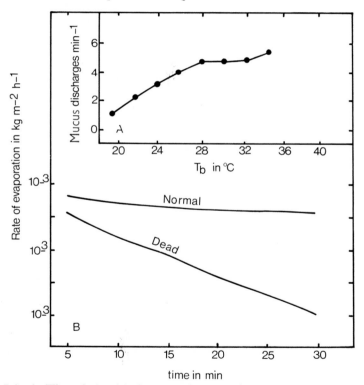

Fig. 5.6. A. The relationship between the mean frequency of discharges from mucous glands and body temperature in the bullfrog (*Rana catesbeiana*) during radiant heating. B. The time course of evaporative water loss in normal and dead frogs with body temperatures of about 27°C. (Redrawn and modified from H. B. Lillywhite, *Z. vergl. Physiol.*, **73**, pp. 84–104, 1971. Berlin–Heidelberg–New York : Springer.)

I   121

Some very recent work on the North American bullfrog (*Rana catesbeiana*) supports this interpretation, and suggests that active control by the nervous system of the rate of discharge of mucus from the cutaneous glands allows this frog to maintain a moist and pliable integument during its characteristic behaviour of basking in direct sunlight. The frequency of discharge of mucus increases as the body temperature rises from 20 to 28°C, and is then stable until 35°C is reached (fig. 5.6). The glands are invested with a layer of myoepithelial cells and are well supplied with nerves and blood vessels. Discharge of the mucus is the result of sympathetic (adrenergic) stimulation, and it is controlled by the central nervous system. For example, damage to the anterior hypothalamus (though not to other brain areas) completely and permanently abolished the discharge of mucus, while with an intact brain there was evidence that receptors located in the peripheral parts of the body might have a facilitating influence on the main central control.

Physiological modulation of the rate of mucus discharge has demonstrable thermoregulatory value in *R. catesbeiana*; elimination of the cutaneous glandular activity results in drying of the skin and increased subcutaneous temperature, so that the mechanism would appear to have adaptive significance in a species which basks extensively in the sun and experiences body temperatures of up to 35°C in nature. One of the most intriguing aspects of this investigation is that it highlights many functional similarities between the amphibian mucous glands and the mammalian sweat glands. The significance of these, however, cannot be assessed at this stage.

5.1.4. *Reptiles*

Of the living orders of reptiles the lizards have been studied to a considerable degree in relation to their thermal environments, but there are only scattered observations on the snakes, tortoises and crocodiles. Among the class as a whole, patterns of thermoregulation characteristic of fish and amphibians are to be found alongside those generally associated with the birds and mammals. All reptiles produce appreciably less metabolic heat for most of the time than do the homoiotherms, and they also lack an effective thermal insulation over the body surface. These features mean that reptiles are typically poikilothermic for much of their lives, although the lability of body temperature and of metabolism may be a significant advantage in the hostile environments that they have successfully invaded. A very rapid exchange of heat with the environment is possible, chiefly by radiation and conduction, and many lizards are able to maintain, during their periods of activity, deep body temperatures that are both as high and as stable as those maintained by endotherms.

By far the most important source of external heat is direct irradiation from the sun. Reptiles using this form of heating commonly tolerate

122

body temperatures similar to those of mammals and birds, while the desert iguana (*Dipsosaurus dorsalis*) has been found still active in nature with a temperature of 45–47°C, which would be lethal for probably all mammals. As with insects, basking behaviour in the sun can be of a rather sophisticated type, involving subtle changes of orientation, raising or lowering of the body relative to the substratum, and altering the shape of the rib cage to increase or minimize the area of the body surface receiving radiation. One of the most impressive examples of the use of solar heat is that of the lizard *Liolaemus multiformis*, which lives at altitudes of up to 4500 metres in the Andes. Air temperatures at this height are frequently below 0°C, but the temperature of the lizards may reach 30°C, warming in the morning at the rate of 1 K min⁻¹. The activity temperature of this species is therefore little different from that of many lizards dwelling in the world's hottest deserts.

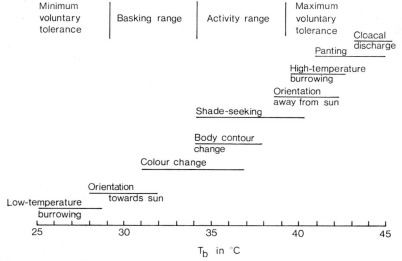

Fig. 5.7. The relationship between selected patterns of behavioural thermo-regulation and body temperature in the horned lizard (*Phrynosoma coronatum*). (Based on data by Heath, *Univ. Calif. Publ. Zool.*, 1965. Originally published by the University of California Press; reprinted by permission of the Regents of the University of California.)

Once optimum temperature has been achieved, basking lizards spend the heat of the day shuttling back and forth between sun and shade, the specific behaviour patterns being related to specific levels of body temperature (fig. 5.7). Desert species may dart rapidly between patches of shade, sometimes on the hind legs only which minimizes contact with the ground which may reach a temperature of 60–70°C. Other lizards dig their bodies into the soft sand, thus contacting the cooler layers that have not been directly exposed to the sun. The role of skin colour in basking lizards has still to be fully elucidated. So far as the visible wave-lengths are concerned it would be advantageous to adopt a dark coloration during the cool hours and a light colour in the hottest part of the day. Some primitive species of lizards can change their body colouring rapidly, and there is evidence that desert species tend to be lighter in colour than those subjected to less severe irradiation.

An example of behavioural thermoregulation which involves basking is also afforded by the Nile crocodile (*Crocodilus niloticus*) which is still common in parts of western Uganda. The animals may be seen in the early hours of the morning basking in the sun on the banks of the river. By mid morning, when the air temperature has risen a good deal above water temperature, they return to the water but frequently lie only half submerged so that the radiant heat from the sun is readily lost to the water by conduction. At dusk the crocodiles leave the river bank and appear to spend the night in the water where the fall in temperature is much less than in the air. In captivity, crocodiles provided with too little water for submergence are frequently found with their mouths partly opened, presumably a means of enhancing evaporative heat loss from the respiratory tract.

Perhaps the most impressive example of the value of rapid warming by solar irradiation is provided by the Galapagos marine iguana (*Amblyrhynchus cristatus*), in which there is also some suggestion of partial physiological control. These animals forage for their food in the relatively cool sea water (about 25°C) around the Galapagos islands, and rely on rapid re-heating to the preferred temperature of about 37°C as soon as they return to the shore. A factor of great interest, however, is that the rate at which the animals heat up is about twice that at which they cool down, when experiments are conducted under standard conditions either in air or in water (fig. 5.8 A). Some mechanism must be operating that helps to increase heat gain and to minimize heat loss. The most likely is a cardiovascular response, for heart rate increases rapidly during heating until the body temperature reaches 35°C, after which it decreases with any further rise (fig. 5.8 B). Nothing is yet known of any changes in blood flow in the marine iguana—this would be the parameter of real significance—but if flow increases with heart rate, as would be most probable, the secondary decline in beating frequency may be an adaptation to maintain body temperature at the optimum for as long as possible, or to reduce the rate of further temperature increase by cutting down the rate of heat transfer from the warm skin to the interior. Essentially the same sort of responses are known to occur in some other lizards, as well as in several species of turtles, while in *Sauromalus varius*, a lizard which lives in the intense heat of the islands in the Gulf of California, the opposite response is also possible, namely accelerated cooling and retarded heating.

124

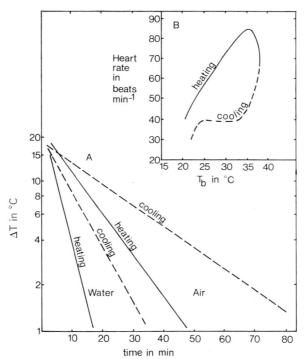

Fig. 5.8. Experiments on the Galapogas marine iguana (*Amblyrynchus cristatus*). A. The difference in temperature (ΔT) between the body and the environment, expressed as a function of time during heating and cooling of the iguana in water and in air at 40 and 20°C. B. Heart rate (HR) in relation to body temperature during heating and cooling. (Redrawn and modified from Bartholomew and Lasiewski, *Comp. Biochem. Physiol.*, 1965.)

It may be that the changes in heart rate which accompany the differences in rates of warming and of cooling are also indications of changes in metabolic activity. Among the reptiles there are, in fact, excellent examples of what we might regard as incipient endothermy. For instance, the large monitor lizards (*Varanus spp.*) have a standard metabolic rate at 37°C only about one-third that of a mammal of the same body mass (700 g). Under such conditions metabolic heat plays no significant part in contributing to body temperature, and the lizards depend almost entirely on ectothermic heat gain. However, during periods of intense activity the metabolic rate may increase by up to five times, an acceleration which anticipates that seen in homoiotherms during exercise, and the heat production then exceeds by about 40 per cent the basal metabolism of the comparable mammal. During such activity much of the heat contributing to the high body temperature must come from metabolism.

Other large reptiles as well, notably the constrictor snakes such as the boas and pythons, but also large tortoises and turtles, can increase heat production by activity and cause body temperature to rise above ambient. The outstanding example is that of the Indian python (*Python molurus*) which consumes 9·3 times as much oxygen when brooding eggs as when not brooding, giving it in the former condition a rate of metabolism which is essentially that of an endotherm. The increased heat production occurs as a result of spasmodic muscular contractions and these appear to set in at an ambient temperature of about 33°C (fig. 5.9). A temperature excess over the environment of up to 4·7 K is achieved as a result of this activity, but the raised metabolism cannot be maintained at below about 25·5°C ambient temperature. The

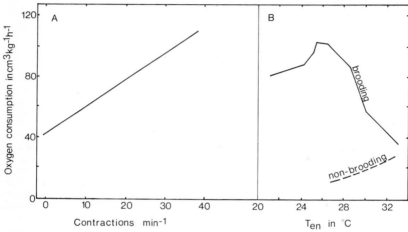

Fig. 5.9. Oxygen consumption in the Indian python (*Python molurus*). A. The relation between heat production and the frequency of spasmodic muscle contractions. B. In the non-brooding python, heat production falls with decreasing environmental temperature ; in the brooding period it increases with falling environmental temperature. (Redrawn and modified from Hutchison *et al.*, *Science*, **151**, pp. 694–696, 11 February 1966. Copyright 1966 by the American Association for the Advancement of Science.)

latter may therefore be analogous to the lower critical temperature of the endotherm, while 33°C may be equivalent to the critical temperature. Indeed, the level of physiological regulation achieved in the brooding python approaches that of the birds and mammals more closely even than does that of the varanid lizards.

These examples suffice to show that reptiles have developed, in relation to their behavioural activities, a significant degree of physiological control of thermoregulation. That the two should proceed together is perhaps as we should expect, for it seems appropriate that physiological abilities should be geared to the requirements imposed by particular behaviour patterns. An instance of this might be the exceptional heat tolerance of the desert iguana, whose behaviour leads it to be most active during the hottest part of the day. We have already seen in Chapter 4 that some lizards, including the iguana, can accelerate the rate at which water is evaporated during heat stress in a manner that appears similar to the panting seen in mammals and birds. Others, for example the box turtle (*Terrapene ornata*), rely on the production of saliva and urine as emergency evaporative cooling methods.

What is of special interest, not least because of its major surprise element, is that evaporative water loss from the skin of reptiles of all orders is now known to be a great deal more rapid than was hitherto realized. Until careful measurements were made it had been customary to attribute to the alleged impermeability of reptilian skin a major role in their ability to adapt to terrestrial conditions, an ability thought to be sharply contrasting with that of amphibians. However, water is lost quite rapidly from the skin of the crocodilian *Caiman sclerops* (at between one-third and one-half the rate of that from amphibian skin), and in several species of lizards, turtles and snakes the major avenue for water loss has now been shown to be the skin rather than the respiratory tract. A significant element in these discoveries is that there appears to be a clear relationship between the rate at which water is lost through the skin and the aridity of the species' habitat. For example, the desert lizard *Sauromalus obesus* loses moisture at only one-twentieth the rate of *Caiman*, and the desert gopher snake (*Pituophis catenifer*) loses less than one-third that of the brown water snake (*Natrix taxispilota*). The discovery of this unexpected permeability of the skin of reptiles should lead to new investigations of its influence on the behavioural patterns of temperature regulation.

Work on the role of the nervous system in controlling temperature responses in reptiles is only just beginning. There are heat-sensitive free nerve endings in the facial pit membrane of rattlesnakes, but otherwise very little is known of the receptor side of the system.

The first hint that the central mechanisms may foreshadow those being extensively investigated in mammals was provided some twenty years ago, when it was shown that warming the forebrain of the turtle *Pseudemys elegans* caused an increase in heart rate and a rise in blood pressure. While these responses could not definitely be viewed as thermoregulatory in nature without concurrent measurements of blood flow in various parts of the body, they nevertheless suggested a special role for this part of the brain in the relationship between temperature and cardiovascular activity.

Much more recently the blue-tongued lizard (*Tiliqua scincoides*) has been used to demonstrate the influence of forebrain temperature changes on behavioural responses concerned with the maintenance of internal body temperature. When given a choice between one of two boxes, either a cold box at 15°C or a hot box at 45°C, the lizards regulate their body temperatures by oscillating between the two. It was found that warming the forebrain artificially to about 41°C by means of implanted thermodes not only reduced the time that the lizards spent in the hot box, but also induced them to leave the box with a lower colonic temperature than was the case when brain temperature was not altered. Conversely, cooling the forebrain caused the lizards to spend more time in the hot box and to leave it at higher colonic temperature than normal (fig. 5.10).

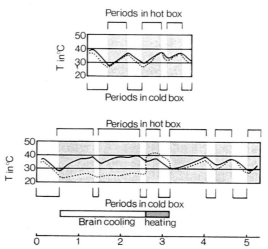

Fig. 5.10. Behavioural thermoregulation in the blue-tongued lizard (*Tiliqua scincoides*). A. Maintenance of a relatively constant colonic temperature (solid line) and brain temperature (dotted line) by shuttling between a hot box (45°C) and a cold box (15°C). B. Cooling the brain prolonged the period in the hot box and increased the colonic temperature at time of exit ; heating the brain had the reverse effects. (Based on work by Hammel *et al.*, *Science*, **156**, pp. 1260–1262, 2 June 1967. Copyright 1967 by the American Association for the Advancement of Science.)

The hypothalamus of *T. scincoides* has also been examined by the complementary technique of recording electrical impulses during local heating and cooling. It was found that some neurons responded by discharging action potentials during warming of the brain and others during its cooling. The former were only about 10 per cent as sensitive to temperature changes as are those of mammals, while the cold-sensitive

128

neurons were about equally responsive. As with the similar experiments on fish, the general conclusion is that there are unmistakable similarities between the mechanisms of regulating body temperature in reptiles and those rather better known in mammals.

5.2. TEMPERATURE RESPONSES OF HOMOIOTHERMS

5.2.1. Adaptive Hypothermia : Hibernation and Torpor

There must be few aspects of animal biology that have aroused more interest and controversy than that of hibernation ; this is amply borne out in the voluminous literature on the subject. In attempting to summarize the features of cardinal importance in the physiology of hibernation, our task is complicated once again by problems of terminology. As in the case of the arbitrary divisions between physiological and behavioural responses to temperature, we shall try to solve this difficulty essentially by ignoring it as one of semantics far more than of biology. We shall therefore treat distinctions such as those between seasonal and diurnal torpor, between torpor and hibernation, and between winter and summer dormancy, as terms used merely for the convenience of human beings. There are few such cases where the categorizations can be adequately defended on strictly physiological grounds, and it might be argued that they are not worth retaining at all. Descriptive expressions such as ' facultative hypothermia ' or ' carnivorean lethargy ', which have been used to delineate various types of torpor, as well as the sub-division of hibernating animals into groups such as stubborn homoiotherms and indifferent homoiotherms, it will also be simplest for us to disregard. Some of these terms undoubtedly have value for the specialist, but for introductory purposes it is extremely doubtful if they are worth using. (See also Section 1.3.5.)

Animals which exhibit periods of torpor as part of their normal life cycle are of special interest in that they combine the advantages both of homoiothermy and of poikilothermy. At favourable times, say during the warm season or merely during the daylight hours, they function as conventional endotherms, while at less favourable times, perhaps during cold weather or at night, they make use of their ability to function as ectotherms, allowing the body temperature to fall towards ambient temperature, and the rate of metabolism to become a fraction of that characteristic of the endothermic period. There is one vital difference between the hibernating endotherm and the true ectotherm. We have already mentioned this in Chapter 1, but it is important enough to be worth repeating. The hibernator is independent of the external source of heat which the ectotherm must have in order to re-warm its body tissues from the torpid to the active state. Thus hibernation represents a change of type but not a failure of thermoregulation.

One definition of hibernation that is broad enough to encompass almost all of its many forms runs as follows : ' a regulated, periodic phenomenon in which body temperatures become readjusted to a new, lower level . . . and heart rate, metabolic rate and other physiological functions show corresponding reductions from which spontaneous or induced arousal to normal levels is possible at all times ' (R. A. Hoffman).

It has been said quite aptly that hibernating animals spend their lives preparing for hibernation, in hibernation, or recovering from hibernation. If at first we consider these phases in various species of rodents and insectivores we shall have a grasp of the phenomenon at perhaps its most representative, and certainly at its best understood. Other mammals, notably the bats and bears, also exhibit seasonal and diurnal periods of torpor, and among birds there are examples of short-lasting torpor in many orders, while in at least one of the nightjars (family Caprimulgidae) there is true seasonal torpor. However, none of these animals has yet been investigated as thoroughly as creatures such as squirrels, mice, hedgehogs and marmots.

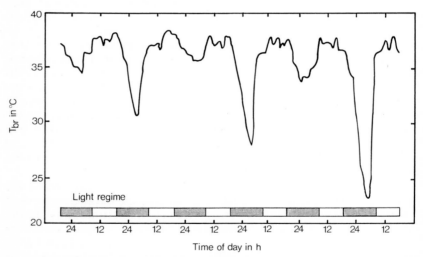

Fig. 5.11. ' Test-drops ' in the brain temperature (T_{br}) of the ground squirrel *Citellus beecheyi* during preparation for hibernation. (After Strumwasser, *Am. J. Physiol.*, 1959.)

Preparation for hibernation begins during the latter part of the favourable weather period. There is a very marked and rapid increase in body mass as food materials are laid down for storage purposes. During this intense period of deposition the respiratory quotient is typically above unity, as fat is formed from carbohydrate. Details of the hormonal changes which are assumed to underlie these physiological

130

preparations are still meagre, although it can safely be said in general that they involve a gradual reduction in endocrine activity prior to the winter sleep. Both morphological and physiological decline have been observed in the pituitary, the thyroid, and the adrenal glands of many hibernating species, and there appears to be a general decrease in sensitivity to cold. This is accompanied by a fall in the basal metabolic rate, a steady increase in fat deposition, and a decline in the body temperature. Most probably the hypothalamus is the master-switch behind the whole process by its regulation of the autonomic nervous system and by its profound influence on the pituitary gland.

Entry into hibernation occurs in several rather different ways in a variety of rodents and insectivores. The most common pattern, seen in the squirrels and marmots for example, is characterized by a series of gradually increasing 'test-drops' of body temperature with complete arousal between each hypothermic period (fig. 5.11). The falls of temperature occur within a few days of cool weather, and the depths to which body temperature and metabolism are allowed to drop apparently depend on the state of preparation. When this is complete the full winter sleep ensues.

Other animals, notably the European garden dormouse (*Eliomys quercinus*), which has a fairly labile deep body temperature at all times, enter hibernation in one rapid decline of temperature (of up to 7 K h^{-1}) within a few days of the cold stimulus. Still others, like the golden hamster (*Mesocricetus auratus*), have high and stable body temperqtures during the period of activity, and enter hibernation only when external conditions become intolerable, rather than on a predictable seasonal basis. Entry occurs typically after a period of 1–3 months in the cold, but then occurs in one major decline of temperature.

One of the most important characteristics in the physiology of hibernation is that body temperature falls to just above ambient temperature and then fluctuates up and down with the latter exactly like that of a poikilotherm. This occurs, however, only within a range of ambient temperature which is high enough on the one hand to prevent freezing of the tissues, and low enough on the other to be below the zone of thermoneutrality of the species. When the animal is threatened by environmental temperature beyond the tolerable range, arousal occurs in part or in full. In many species, temperatures near freezing are countered, not by full awakening, but by an increase in metabolism just sufficient to prevent destruction of tissue. Even when full arousal occurs, marked by a very rapid rise in metabolic heat production and a return to normal body temperature, torpor may be regained after a relatively short period of time. In fact, many hibernating species always exhibit periods of torpor alternating with periods of activity, even when they are not subjected to any recognizable environmental stress.

Metabolism during hibernation is very low, allowing long periods when the intake of food is unnecessary. Levels between 1 and 3 per cent of the normal basal metabolism have commonly been measured, and there is a respiratory quotient in the region of 0·7, indicating the utilization of fat. Breathing frequency is equally slow, about $4 \, min^{-1}$ in the ground squirrel (*Citellus citellus*), compared with rates between 100 and 200 min^{-1} during normal activity. Long periods may occur when the movements cease altogether, only to be followed by gasps of irregular amplitude. Cardiovascular parameters such as heart rate and blood pressure fall dramatically, although in some species the latter recovers later on as a result of selective vasoconstriction and an increase in the viscosity of the blood. Much blood may be stored, more or less out of the circulation in organs like the spleen and liver, but the dangers of clotting in stagnant or slowly circulating blood seem to be avoided by

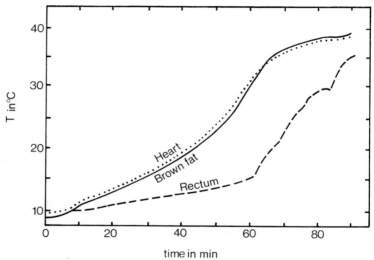

Fig. 5.12. The rate of rise in temperature of various parts of the body in the golden-mantled ground squirrel (*Citellus lateralis*) during arousal from hibernation. (Redrawn and modified from Hayward *et al.*, *Ann. N.Y. Acad. Sci.*, 1965.)

a reduced efficiency in the mechanism of coagulation. One of the chief factors distinguishing hibernating animals from the non-hibernators seems to be the ability of the heart to continue its functions at very low temperature.

Body mass, which may have doubled during the preparatory period, declines gradually throughout hibernation, and the degree of loss may be related to the number and length of the arousal periods prior to the final awakening in spring. It has been calculated that some 90 per cent

132

of the total heat production of hibernation occurs during arousal and only the remainder during torpor. This gives some idea of the extent of the physiological economy achieved.

Arousal itself is the result of an enormous rise in metabolic rate that is entirely beyond the capacity of animals that do not hibernate. The body temperature may increase at the rate of 20 K h^{-1} and such dramatic changes are accompanied by great activity in the cardiovascular and respiratory systems, probably resulting from massive stimulation by the sympathetic nervous system. A major source of the heat production is the brown fat deposit (often called the ' hibernating gland '), as is shown by its rapid rise in temperature compared with that of the abdominal viscera (fig. 5.12). Intense shivering thermogenesis may also occur.

Physiologically, the difference between the seasonal hibernation of squirrels and the diurnal torpor of bats is almost certainly quantitative rather than qualitative. The bats have highly variable body temperatures at all times of the day. The level is regulated very largely by activity, so that as soon as the bat rests its temperature falls to that of the surroundings. Of course, those bats that undergo seasonal as well as daily periods of torpor must prepare for the former by storing fat just as do the rodents, whereas the diurnal periods require no such special preparation.

Birds which can use hypothermia as a means of reducing their requirements of energy tend to be those that feed on insects or on nectar in situations where the supplies may become temporarily depleted. The best studied are certain species of humming birds, in which feeding is impossible at night, and where the pattern is one of nocturnal torpor (fig. 5.13). It has been calculated that there is a saving of some 25 per cent in energy requirements for each night that is spent in torpor compared to the demands if normal temperature were maintained.

At the present time it seems that one important difference between hibernation in birds and mammals is that arousal in the former class cannot occur in ambient temperatures much below 10°C. This seems to be true even for the Caprimulgidae in which long-term seasonal hibernation occurs. However, a great deal of work will be needed before we can be certain of this distinction, especially in view of the fact that birds are known to be torpid with body temperatures as low as 3·5°C in the Andes.

Finally, we should note that the seasonal and diurnal torpor observed in many northern-latitude bears, while it is often put into a special category, is unlikely to be fundamentally different from that of the animals we have already considered. It is again probably a difference only of degree. The reason why the body temperature of a large bear (sometimes more than 200 kg in mass) could not be varied with the

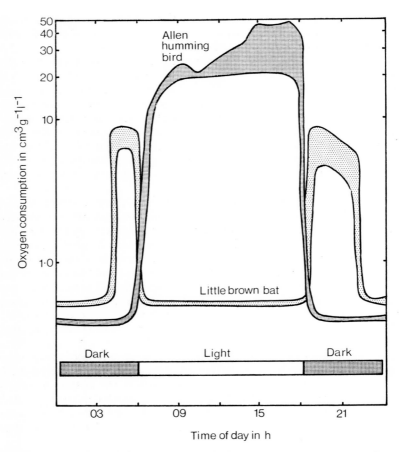

Fig. 5.13. Diagrammatic representation of the metabolic rate (oxygen consumption) of the Allen humming bird (*Selasphorus sasin*) and the little brown bat (*Myotis lucifugus*) during activity and torpor. An indication of the variability of metabolism during activity is given by the width of the shaded areas. (Redrawn and modified from Bartholomew in *Animal Function: Principles and Adaptations*, by M. S. Gordon. Copyright 1968, The Macmillan Company.)

flexibility of that of a bird or mammal of only a few grams, is simply that the enormous bulk would take far too long to cool down and to re-heat. A mouse or humming bird may heat up as rapidly as 1 K min⁻¹, but an animal of even moderate size could not approach this rate. Unless cooling and warming can occur quickly, the use of diurnal torpor is impossible because no time would be left for the intense activities of the waking period. Furthermore, raising the body temperature of a really large animal by, say, 25 K would consume at least as much energy as the animal would require throughout the entire day if it maintained its body temperature at a relatively constant level. Male polar bears do not, in fact, hibernate at all.

Dormancy that occurs at relatively high environmental temperatures (aestivation) is also unlikely to be physiologically distinguishable from that occurring in cold weather. The ultimate stimulus, insufficient food or water, is the same in either case, and the adaptive advantage is therefore that of energy conservation. The functional changes do not differ in kind, and there are several species which exhibit torpor in the heat as well as in the cold.

5.2.2. *Typical Responses of Birds and Mammals*

As with the subject of hibernation, it would be all too easy for us to devote an entire chapter to the behavioural responses of homoiotherms to changes in environmental temperature. A great deal of descriptive material is available, much of it of considerable interest, but it is only in the last few years that a beginning has been made on a more rigorous examination of thermoregulatory behaviour. During the same time there has been an increasing appreciation of the fact that, when given freedom of choice, homoiotherms generally rely more on behaviour than on physiological responses to regulate their body temperatures. Behaviour can often bring about a desired change more quickly than can a physiological effector, and often at a fraction of the cost. Unfortunately, it is technically difficult to allow animals enough freedom to behave normally if precise physiological measurements are to be made at the same time, and this may be one of the reasons why most theories of thermoregulatory control have been based on physiological evidence alone, to the detriment of behavioural studies. We now appreciate that if we are to understand the total picture of thermoregulation in homoiotherms we must investigate the total range of responses available. It therefore follows that if we take a cat or a pigeon into the laboratory and examine its reactions to thermal stress without offering it the freedom to behave as naturally as possible, we are dealing with a biological artifact hardly better than the frog or lizard that we considered earlier.

Let us begin by briefly considering the most important behavioural responses that have been described in mammals and birds, and go on later to look at some of the ways in which such behaviour can be analysed experimentally. Changes of body posture, both in individual animals and in groups, can have significant effects on heat loss or conservation. Many animals modify their heat transfer at different ambient temperatures by spreading out the limbs when warm and holding them close to the body when cold. The effective radiating surface is changed by this means in new-born pigs from 76 per cent at 30°C to 67 per cent at 20°C. The fowl, merely by plunging its head into its feathers, reduces its rate of heat loss by 12 per cent, while sitting on the legs to eliminate exposure of the unfeathered portions causes a reduction of more than 30 per cent compared to standing up. Conversely, in the heat fowls hold their wings out and away from the sides of the body, and occasionally may be seen making gentle fanning movements, thereby increasing the surface area for radiant losses and providing forced air movement for convection.

Similar responses occur in animals in groups. Huddling together is a fundamental behaviour pattern in new-born puppies and mice, and it persists to adulthood in pigs. Domestic chicks can reduce their metabolic rates by up to 15 per cent by huddling, while in many adult birds this sort of behaviour is commonly seen during roosting. Thus group associations have been noted in the wren (*Troglodytes troglodytes*) and in the European short-toed tree creeper (*Certhia brachdactyla*) on cold nights, when the number of birds involved may be estimated only by the tail feathers projecting out from the mass. In the sub-antarctic environment of Macquarie Island, large groups of gentoo pigeons (*Pygoscelis papua*) may be seen gathered closely together on the sheltered side of rocks or grassy tussocks at night time, even though this species does not form the rookeries characteristic of many penguins.

Postural changes are often accompanied by alterations in the insulation of the coat by means of erection or collapse of the hair or feathers. For instance many birds raise their feathers in the cold and sleek them when hot ; it has been shown in the Barbary dove (*Streptopelia risoria*) that feather movements serve as a rapid and effective means of temperature regulation, and that feather posture is governed by hypothalamic temperature.

Selection of micro-habitats or niches, such as holes in trees, burrows in the ground or buttresses against the wind, obviously play a significant part in the lives of many animals. In nature, however, it is often difficult to distinguish such behaviour with certainty from that associated with the avoidance of predators. It is often said that birds utilize protective niches a good deal less than mammals, although once again this may reflect no more than the differences in our knowledge of the two classes. Many small birds that live in close association with man use his buildings and other structures for protection against the elements, and among arctic species there are some which burrow into the snow.

Postural changes are also used by species of birds which conserve metabolic energy by using radiant heat from the sun. The white-crowned sparrow (*Zonotrichia leucophrys*) consumes less food at low ambient temperature if allowed to bask in the sun, while in the brown-headed cowbird (*Molothrus ater*) oxygen consumption may be reduced by up to 26 per cent in dark individuals, but by only 6 per cent in light-coloured ones which reflect more of the visible range of the spectrum. In the same species basking behaviour can lower the critical environmental temperature from 35 to 25°C. Finally, the roadrunner (*Geococcyx californianus*) not only saves some 40 per cent of its metabolic energy expenditure by basking, but also makes use of the sun to raise the body temperature to normal following periods of adaptive hypothermia.

In situations where the heat of the sun imposes a thermal stress, postural adjustments may also have an important influence on heat transfer. One example is that of the black-footed albatross (*Diomedea nigripes*) which balances on its heels when exposed to direct sunlight and, by orientating itself with its back to the sun, manages to expose the large, well-vascularized feet to relatively cool air so that heat loss by convection and radiation is maximal. At the same time the posture presumably minimizes the transfer of heat to the body by conduction from the hot ground. Parental behaviour is also important in species subjected to high temperatures, where the young are protected from solar irradiation in the day as well as being provided with body heat at night. The mallee-fowl (*Leipoa ocellata*) in Australia provides a particularly striking example of the role of the parent. The eggs are deposited in mounds of soil and decaying matter, the temperature of incubation being attained as a result of the processes of decomposition. The adult birds appear to be capable of assessing the correct temperature, for they thrust their bills deeply into the mound and then either remove some of the covering material or add to it, apparently according to whether the eggs are too warm or too cool.

Large animals which cannot so easily use burrows and natural shelters as protection against heat or cold do, on the other hand, have the advantage of being more mobile ; they are more readily able to migrate out of the areas where thermal conditions are intolerable. When this is impossible, large animals still possess the natural physical advantages that go with size. They can utilize to the full the benefits of a thick insulating coat, and when necessary can store large quantities of heat without suffering too great a degree of hyperthermia. There is also a greater tolerance of water shortage because severe dehydration sets in much more slowly.

The advantages of locomotor activity are best shown by birds which, by their ability to fly, enjoy an unequalled freedom to avoid severe conditions. At its most impressive this is achieved by migration over great distances, but some birds, without leaving the habitat, avoid intense heat by soaring flight which consumes little energy, minimizes the effects of radiation reflected from the ground, and accelerates heat loss by convection. These advantages presumably outweigh the likely effects of increased exposure to the direct heat of the sun.

It has recently been shown that very great increases in convective heat loss may occur in flight. Indeed, it seems that sustained flight at even moderate temperatures would be impossible without effective alterations in the posture, and hence in the insulation, of the feathers, for the metabolic heat production during flight can be very great. An increase of up to 15-fold over basal metabolism occurs in pigeons flying at 58 km h^{-1}; the raised body temperature which results levels off at about 44·5°C (2 K or so above the resting level) over an ambient temperature range of 4 to 30°C. A marked increase in evaporative heat loss occurs during flight only at high temperatures. Measurements on the budgerigar (*Melopsittacus undulatus*), for instance, suggest that level flight at 35 km h^{-1} may increase metabolic rate by nearly 13 times over the basal level at air temperatures from 20 to 37°C. Non-evaporative heat losses were estimated to be 85 and 82 per cent of the total at 30 and 20°C respectively. Even at 37°C air temperature, evaporative loss seemed to account for only 47 per cent of the heat produced, although at this temperature severe hyperthermia occurred after 20 minutes.

A far smaller fraction of the total heat loss may therefore be by evaporation of water than was formerly believed, and this must be a major factor in the ability of birds to undertake long migration flights without drinking. On this important question, calculations on the budgerigar (the only bird for which data are presently available, although this species does not, in fact, migrate) indicate that, if the bird can tolerate a level of dehydration amounting to 15 per cent of its body mass, it should be able to fly continuously for 14 hours, losing about 1·1 per cent of its mass per hour. This would permit it a range of up to 500 km. In nature, some birds of smaller size than the budgerigar fly a good deal further than this, while many larger species can fly up to four times as far and a few ten times as far without suffering intolerable dehydration. Exactly how this is achieved physiologically is still unknown.

The intake of food and water is closely related to the regulation of body temperature, a fact that we all know from common experience, and one that has been borne out experimentally by the demonstration that the hypothalamus is intimately involved in all three regulations. All animals seem to eat more as ambient temperature falls below the critical temperature, consuming the extra energy necessary to stoke the fires of metabolism. The quality of the food may also be changed when a choice is available. For example, turkeys consume more wheat and maize (high energy foods) than prepared mash when exposed to cold, the reverse when exposed to heat. Consumption of water usually moves in the opposite direction to that of food, increasing especially rapidly in the zone of physical regulation, when it is used not only for the physiological mechanisms of evaporation, but also in some animals for throwing over parts of the body to enhance this form of cooling. This is particularly obvious in fowls, which will dip their beaks deeply into water and then throw a good deal of it over their wattles and combs where evaporation occurs. If pigs are provided with a good wallow in hot weather they are able to evaporate moisture from the skin, as a result of coating themselves with muddy water, at a similar rate to that at which it is actively secreted in many sweating species.

5.2.2.1. *Operant conditioning of thermal responses*

There has been much work in recent years designed to determine the sort of thermal conditions an animal chooses of its own volition when provided with a means of altering its environment. We have already encountered one rather remarkable example of such behaviour in goldfish, which are capable of maintaining a tolerably cool environment against a constant heat stimulus, by letting in cold water to their aquarium. The great bulk of such work, however, has been done with mammals, and the investigation of other animals has only just begun.

When an animal is required to learn an operation by which it may influence its own environment, and is then allowed to perform the operation freely so as to change the environment in a given direction and by a given amount, it is said to be undergoing operant conditioning. This technique was developed largely by B. F. Skinner at Harvard University, as a means of testing the role of behavioural drives or motivation in a wide variety of situations, most often in relation to feeding. In operant conditioning the animal takes an active part in the learning process, in contrast to the classical form of conditioning described by Ivan Pavlov (1849–1936), where the response is entirely governed by the autonomic nervous system, and to that extent at least can be said to be passive. To stimulate the active learning process of operant conditioning the animal's response must be ' reinforced ' by a reward which results from its action.

Experiments on mice, rats, pigs, monkeys and other mammals have shown quite conclusively that when such animals are in a cold environment they can easily learn to press a switch which turns on a radiant lamp and provides reinforcement in the form of a brief period of wamrth. The lamp is arranged to switch off automatically after a few seconds, so that the animal must continually respond by pressing the switch if it is to obtain significant benefit from its action. A considerable amount of information on the conditions the animal would itself prefer is gained if the frequency of the responses is recorded.

In pigs, the rate of responding in such an experiment declines as ambient temperatures rise above about 10°C (fig. 5.14). Further experiments have refined these initial observations. For example, pigs with access to radiant heat are able to maintain basal metabolic rates at environmental temperatures well below the normal critical temperature. Furthermore, if restricted to a relatively low food intake they will respond much faster than other pigs given ample food.

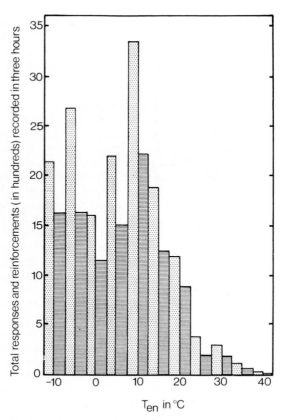

Fig. 5.14. Behavioural thermoregulation in the pig. Total responses (pushing a switch) and reinforcements (3-second burst of infra-red heat) plotted against environmental temperature. Responses (stippled) are more numerous than reinforcements (notched) because those made during the infra-red heating were without effect. (After Baldwin and Ingram, *Physiol. Behav.*, 1967.)

Perhaps it is not surprising that the method of operant conditioning should have been used in conjunction with heating and cooling of the hypothalamus. Cooling the hypothalamus of a pig below normal results in an increase in the rate at which the radiant heat is turned on at a given environmental temperature ; warming the hypothalamus has the reverse effect. In the squirrel monkey (*Saimiri sciurea*) artificial changes in hypothalamic temperature will elicit work designed to change the environmental temperature in the opposite direction, while a highly ingenious technique has shown that rats will respond to produce changes in their own hypothalamic temperature (by altering the temperature of water perfusing implanted thermodes), the frequency of the responses being proportional to the displacement of skin temperature and hypothalamic temperature from their normal values. All of these findings fit in rather well with information on temperature regulation derived by more conventional means, and they have contributed significantly to our overall understanding.

5.2.3. *The Special Case of Man*

With a little thought it will be quite easy to see that many of the behavioural responses that we expect from animals are equally characteristic of own own species. On the whole, man utilizes such responses in preference to the more fundamental physiological ones, so that in the comfortable life possible for many people in the rich countries of the world, responses such as shivering are relatively uncommon. The special characteristic of man, however, is his ability to influence his immediate environment to an extent unapproached by other animals. The result of this is that he is able to inhabit any region on earth, and now even to visit the hostile surface of the moon.

In extreme cold man could not possibly survive without his clothing, shelter and artificial heating. In this respect Eskimos differ in no important respect from the modern polar explorer. The skins of arctic animals provide an insulation as effective as that of the best polar uniforms, and the typical igloo meets most of the requirements considered essential by our advanced technology for a polar hut. The hard snow forming the walls of the igloo traps countless insulating pockets of air ; the inside layer of snow melts somewhat under the influence of the Eskimo's oil lamp, refreezes and forms a hard reflecting layer which conserves radiant heat (and is equivalent to the aluminium foil surface for the interior of modern buildings) ; and the outer surface of the igloo becomes thoroughly encrusted by the wind into an airtight shield. Thus it is true to say that man inhabits the polar regions by avoiding the rigours of the polar conditions.

The same is often true of man in a hot environment. The sweating mechanism is, of course, highly efficient as a means of heat loss, yet it depends critically on the availability of water. Thus the main responses which enable man to live successfully in the desert tend to be cultural and technological. The provision of shelter is often the most vital need, for it eliminates the great burden of direct insolation. Unfortunately, some forms of shelter minimize one problem only to create another. This tends to occur because the material that is used to shut out the sun has, for practical reasons, to be closer to the human occupants than is really desirable, and this may severely reduce air movement. On the other hand, a dwelling that is constructed only with maximum ventilation in mind may, even in the equatorial regions, have the disadvantage of being too cool at night, for the critical temperature of naked man is between 27 and 29°C, a level which is seldom maintained throughout the 24 hours at any point on earth. Of course, modern man is able to counter the coolness more successfully, while during the heat of the day he may resort to methods of refrigeration and air conditioning. The introduction of air conditioning in the United States has been an important factor in reducing mortality during exceptionally hot spells.

Interest in the relationship between the thermal environment of man and his comfort, his health and the efficiency of his working performance, led to attempts to define the conditions that were optimal in office and industry. Very warm conditions were known to lead to a decline in performance, while very cold ones caused a sharp increase in respiratory infections. Thus there arose the concept of the 'ideal' temperature as that at which optimal comfort was experienced. The impression of comfort is very largely subjective, and estimates of ideal temperature have usually been made on the basis of the maximum number of votes for comfort given by a group of people subject to a range of conditions. Such assessments are bound to be influenced by the state of acclimatization of the subjects, as well as by more subtle factors such as the varying standards of comfort recognized as acceptable by people of different age and economic status and with different expectations.

In physiological terms, ideal comfort is usually said to be experienced when the skin temperature averages 33°C and when there is minimal exchange of heat in the body tissues and a minimum rate of evaporation. Such conditions are best achieved at complete rest, which is of small value in practical terms, although fortunately it is possible to predict ideal temperatures for various levels of metabolism above basal. Since there is always a considerable range of subjective preference among individuals, there is bound to be a considerable range of ideal temperature. Things are further complicated by the fact that men tend to dress more suitably for cool conditions than do women, while women are often more comfortably dressed in the heat than are men. Nevertheless, in light clothing and under conditions of complete rest, both sexes commonly find 25°C to be about the ideal temperature. During an activity such as rapid typing (which raises the metabolic rate by about 40 per cent) the ideal temperature falls to about 21°C, and it would be substantially lower still during heavy work.

CHAPTER 6
mechanisms controlling body temperature

Any control system consists of three essential components. First, there must be a measuring device which detects changes that are relevant to the system. Second, there must be some mechanism for assessing the significance of single changes and integrating the overall effects of many. Finally, there have to be appropriate effector mechanisms which can respond to the instructions of the integrator, and can alter the behaviour of the controlling system in the most suitable way.

So far we have concentrated almost all our attention on the last of these components, the effector mechanisms such as shivering, sweating and behavioural reactions. To some extent this is because it is the effector responses that most readily come to mind when we think of temperature regulation ; most of them are familiar to us, and this may be one reason why they have been investigated by physiologists so much more thoroughly than the other two components of the controlling system. Perhaps the main reason for this, however, is that the effector mechanisms are technically the simplest to investigate. The sensory and integrating aspects are a great deal more elusive, and although they have been studied for well over a hundred years it is only in the last decade or so that definitive knowledge has emerged. Indeed, even this claim may be an over-statement in the case of the sensory side, where our techniques still appear far too crude to unravel the extraordinary complexities (probably molecular) which differentiate the various receptors. In the case of the central nervous integration, however, there have been major advances in recent years and these will form the greater part of this chapter.

Before we examine the role of the nervous system in governing the regulation of body temperature in adult animals, it will be useful to look briefly at how such regulation develops in the young.

6.1. ONTOGENY OF CONTROL

One thing that is quite clear about the development of thermo-regulatory abilities in young animals is that there is enormous specific variation. At one extreme there are those animals which are exceedingly susceptible to chilling in the early post-natal period ; outside a relatively narrow range of ambient temperature they are essentially ectothermic. At the other extreme are animals which exhibit high cold-resistance and virtually fully-formed thermoregulatory capabilities at birth. Birds (and, less often, mammals also) in the first category are termed altricial and those in the second are called precocial. Needless to say, it is important that we do not think rigidly in terms of the two types, for there are many species which are neither wholly the one nor wholly the other. Precocial development is the first in the evolutionary sense, and is found in some modern reptiles, whereas the value of the altricial form may be more in terms of protection against predators than of heat balance. However, there could be advantages in the economy of energy resources during the period of rapid growth ; the young animal, instead of utilizing energy for regulation of body temperature, relies at first on warmth from its parents, so that a greater proportion of the food consumed may be converted into the materials for building the body.

The functional basis of the development of thermoregulation is still poorly understood, but at least four factors are widely believed to play a part. Of these, perhaps the most fundamental is the decrease in the ratio of surface area to body mass which occurs during the early days of rapid growth. Concurrently with this there is commonly the appearance or development of hair or feathers, so that these two factors have the effect of increasing the insulation against loss of metabolic heat. A third factor is the increase in thermogenic capacity by the development of the shivering mechanism or the metabolism of brown fat. Finally, the least understood factor of all is presumed to be the gradual refinement of the neural and hormonal mechanisms underlying the temperature regulating system.

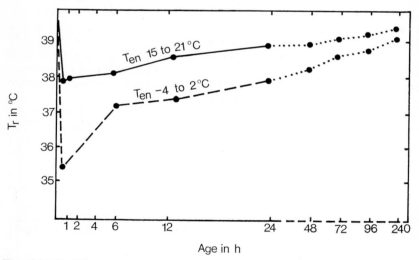

Fig. 6.1. Rectal temperature (T_r) in a warm and cold environment in young pigs. (Redrawn from Newland et al., J. anim. Sci., 1952.)

144

Among the mammals, small species like the mouse and rat appear to be adapted to tolerate hypothermia during the first week or so of life. This obviously has considerable survival value, since low temperatures are suffered whenever the mother leaves the nest. Other species also show cold-tolerance of a lesser degree. At birth itself, the deep body temperature of new-born mammals invariably falls precipitously from the normal level of 37–39°C which was possible *in utero* (fig. 6.1). The absolute rate of metabolism is reduced by this fall of temperature, and it remains for several days lower than the level characteristic of later life ; however, it is important to realize that acceleration of heat production is possible even during the first day of post-natal life

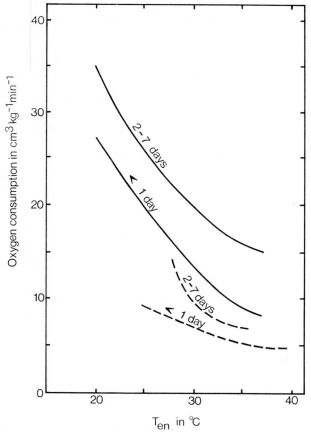

Fig. 6.2. Oxygen consumption in relation to environmental temperature in new-born pigs (solid lines) and human infants (broken lines). (Redrawn from Mount, in *Swine in Biomedical Research*, by C. K. Bustad and R. O. McClellan, Battelle, 1966.)

(fig. 6.2.). The length of time taken for the metabolic rate to attain the level of adulthood appears to be related to the degree of maturity at birth. It is 14 days in the rat which is born naked and helpless, but only a few hours in the lamb which is quickly active and on its feet. This is not merely a feature of body size, as is shown by the fact that metabolism in the guinea pig is at the adult level immediately upon birth.

In the protected environment normally provided for the new-born human infant a body temperature of 36–37°C is maintained without difficulty, that is, without resort to the sustained and costly metabolism of brown fat. The heat-loss effectors, such as sweating and vaso-dilatation, are available from an early age, as can sometimes be seen in very young infants which have been excessively insulated with clothes and bedding, when droplets of sweat appear on the forehead. More commonly, of course, there is danger of cold-stress, especially since a baby lying in its cot may, because of air movement and low radiant temperature, be in an effective environment that is a good deal cooler than that indicated by a simple thermometer measuring air temperature. When cold, the new-born baby can elicit vasoconstriction as well as a raised heat production by means of brown fat metabolism.

One of the best indicators of thermoregulatory capacity in any homoiotherm is the gradual decline of the critical temperature as the surface insulation and metabolic response reach the adult level of efficiency. Figures for the pig, for example, show that the critical temperature is about 34°C in the new-born and 25°C in the adult.

The situation in birds is not markedly different from that in mammals. Altricial species like the passerines are naked and helpless at hatching and capable of little or no thermoregulation. The ability to regulate, however, often develops remarkably quickly and is typically complete within one or two weeks. Such development is even more rapid in precocial species such as the chick of the domestic fowl, but even here thermoregulation is by no means at the adult level on hatching. Despite the coat of down and the obviously well developed neuromuscular functions, chicks are highly susceptible to cold during the first day and a half of life, and are not really good regulators until at least five days of age (fig. 6.3). Nevertheless, the behavioural activities available to precocial species make a significant difference under natural conditions, particularly in relation to the parent birds which will shelter the young from the stresses of both heat and cold.

It is undoubtedly among the altricial species that most advances have been made in understanding the four main factors concerned in the ontogeny of thermoregulation. In several species of sparrow at six days of age, the ratio of surface to volume is 50 per cent less than at hatching, and meanwhile the feathers have developed substantially and so minimize the loss of heat. Furthermore, the improved area/mass ratio is partly the result of the growth of tissues which are concerned

146

in the production of heat, most notably of the skeletal muscles, but also of the heart and liver, which increase in size more quickly than the body as a whole. Thus the metabolic capability increases at the same time

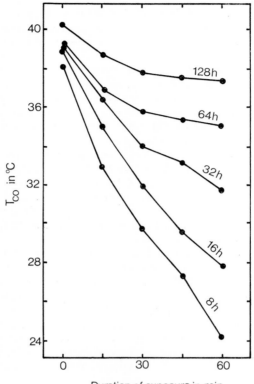

Fig. 6.3. The response of colonic temperature (T_{co}) in chicks of the domestic fowl exposed to cold. The chicks were removed from an incubator at 35·5°C and exposed individually to an environmental temperature of 10°C. (Redrawn from Wekstein and Zolman, *Proc. Soc. exptl Biol. Med.*, 1967.)

as the insulation. There is almost no information as yet on the development of the nervous system during this crucial period, but thyroid activity in young nestlings seems to exceed that of adults, and this could be a factor underlying the increased metabolism.

6.2. *PERIPHERAL RECEPTORS*

No one will doubt the existence of receptors in the skin that are sensitive to warmth and cold. The sensations with which they provide

147

us form an important part of both physiological and behavioural temperature regulation, and represent the most effective means of anticipating and avoiding extremes of temperature. Despite our familiarity with thermal sensations from the skin, more than a hundred years of effort by physiologists have failed to solve many of the fundamental questions about how they function and to what extent they are important, in comparison, say, with the receptors deep in the brain.

Sensations, transmitted from receptors in the periphery, can be studied only in man because animals cannot tell us what they experience. We distinguish four types of cutaneous sensation, heat, cold, touch and pain, although in some circumstances it is difficult to separate them. Many years ago it was found that if the skin is explored with minute rods which are either hot or cold as judged by the subjective sensations they induce, various spots on the skin show different sensitivities to the different stimuli. Thus there are warm spots, cold spots, touch spots and so on, and it was soon claimed by histologists working at the end of last century that particular skin regions could be identified with the receptors sensitive to the various stimuli. At the time, this supposed link was welcomed as a major discovery which appeared to clarify many of the functional problems associated with skin sensations. Detailed diagrams were published which purported to show that the thermal sensations are attributable to specialized capsules which surround the nerve endings. The so-called Krause end-bulbs were said to subserve cold, and the Ruffini corpuscles were assigned to warmth, while the free uncapsulated nerve endings were stated to be responsible for pain. Unfortunately, these alleged connexions between structure and function were made without experimental support, and they have now been entirely discredited. It is sometimes said that the best evidence for the role of the Krause and Ruffini capsules consisted in the belief that Germans are cold and Italians warm.

These early ideas were proved false largely by the work of G. Weddell. He would identify warm or cold spots on his own skin, have the skin cut out, and examine it histologically. No correlation could be found between the sensation experienced and the structure of nerve endings and, indeed, there were patches of skin that contained nothing but free nerve endings and yet which responded to all four types of sensation. In further experiments it was shown that the occurrence of the capsule-like structures in the skin increased with the age of the subject. This observation suggested that the capsules might be the result merely of past damage to that part of the skin and that they served no physiological function ; they are now, in fact, regarded as artifacts, and only free nerve endings in the skin are believed to be concerned in the collection of information. Because the endings cannot be distinguished histologically, however, we should not think of them as being physiologically all the same. As we shall see shortly, recent indications make it quite clear that this is not the case.

A good deal is now known about thermal receptors in human skin, although the knowledge tends to be of a general nature rather than in terms of specific details of the operation of individual receptors. Obviously, the greatest technical difficulty results from the minute size of a single nerve fibre, and it has been only since about 1950 that methods have been available for tackling the problem at all. A tiny electrode is placed in the nerve passing towards the spinal cord from a

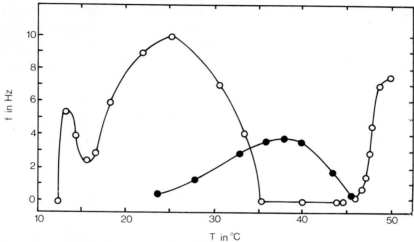

Fig. 6.4. The frequency of electrical impulses in nerve fibres from a cold receptor (open circles) and a warm receptor (solid circles) in the cat's tongue as affected by local temperature. (Redrawn and modified from Zotterman, *Ann. Rev. Physiol.*, 1953.)

cutaneous receptor, the latter is then stimulated in various ways, and the resultant changes in electrical potential are displayed on an oscilloscope. As always seems to happen in research on the nervous system, the preliminary experiments have shown that the old division into four distinct types of sensation is an oversimplification. Receptors have been found which respond to a wide range of different stimuli, but so far as we are concerned three of these are of most interest. One type responds to high skin temperature by accelerating the rate of electrical discharges it produces ; another responds with similar discharges, but to low skin temperature (fig. 6.4) ; a third variety gives a continuous barrage of impulses only when stimulated by strong pressure or heat. The last type of receptor may be responsible for transmitting the sensation of pain.

Much of the basic work has actually been carried out on the tongue of cats and dogs. Although the tongue is not normally used in temperature reception, there are good reasons for believing that the results are not grossly different from those that might be obtained with human skin. For example, the results from electrophysiological investigations on animals and subjective tests on human subjects both reveal that thermal sensations within a limited range of temperature (about 20–40°C) fade away as the receptors appear to adapt. Above and below this range continuous barrages of electrical impulses are recorded and the sensations of cold or warmth do not diminish. Similarly, the strange phenomenon of 'paradoxical cold' is at least superficially explained by modern physiological methods. Thus, if the temperature of a stimulating probe applied to a known cold spot on the skin is gradually raised, the sensation of cold fades to one of indifference at about 36°C, only to recur as a sensation of cold when the temperature reaches as high as 45°C. Studies on the dog's tongue show that the cold receptors in this organ (which, of course, is normally at a somewhat higher temperature than the human skin) cease to discharge impulses at 35–40°C, but commence again at between 45 and 50°C (fig. 6.4). Presumably in normal life the sensation of paradoxical cold is suppressed by stimuli from nearby warm spots.

In human skin, sensitivity to thermal stimuli varies according to region. The face and hands are generally speaking the most sensitive to both heat and cold, although the forehead is very much more cold-sensitive than warm-sensitive. In fact, cold spots in human skin appear to be about 4 to 10 times as common as warm spots, and this discovery fits in very nicely with modern ideas of how the regulating system operates in man (Section 6.4.2). The dominance of cold receptors may also explain the fact that the sensation of cold persists for many seconds after removal of the cold stimulus, as long, it seems, as the receptors are below their threshold temperature for discharging impulses.

A naked animal such as man can readily sense changes of environmental temperature by means of the thermal receptors scattered over his entire skin, but a heavily furred or feathered animal might be expected to have more difficulty. It was therefore no surprise to find that heating large areas of the feathered skin in the fowl does not elicit the panting response until the heating is so prolonged as to cause a rise in the deep body temperature. This contrasts with results on the relatively thinly furred ox, where panting can be elicited from a rise in skin temperature alone. In some other mammals there are specialized areas of skin which are temperature-sensitive. Thus, gentle warming of the rabbit's ears, which affects neither brain nor general skin temperature, inhibits shivering and reduces oxygen consumption and deep body temperature. The scrotal skin is another example ; when heated in the ram it elicits panting, even when the deep body temperature falls by up to 2 K as a result of the evaporative heat loss. Indeed, the scrotum is a particularly good example of local control, its main function apparently being to maintain a steady temperature for sperm development which, however, is slightly lower than the deep body temperature. This is achieved by suspending the testes outside the abdomen and by adjustments to the muscles and blood vessels of the scrotal wall. Finally, in man, the familiar experience of ' gustatory sweating ' which follows strong stimulation of the mouth and tongue by pungent substances such as pepper, mustard or curry, is thought to be induced by the false sensation of local heat. It seems likely that pain receptors may be involved.

6.3. CENTRAL RECEPTORS

More than a century ago experimental physiologists had already started to investigate the hypothesis put forward by L. Bergmann in 1845 that temperature regulation is dependent on thermally sensitive receptors in the brain. The idea was supported when it was shown that artificial warming or cooling of the brain, usually by means of the carotid blood supply, led to normal thermoregulatory responses which apparently attempted to correct the deviation. Gradually the specific area involved was narrowed down by experiments in which localized damage to brain tissue was related to subsequent deficiencies in thermo-regulatory performance, until in more recent times it has become universally accepted that the hypothalamus is the cerebral structure of particular importance. Damage to the anterior part of the hypothalamus was often found to result in a deficiency of the heat-loss mechanisms, whereas damage to the posterior part caused interference with the mechanisms of heat production. There thus arose the idea of two separate thermosensitive centres in the hypothalamus, the one control-ling physical and the other chemical regulation. Although there are significant variations among different species in the way of functioning and the relative importance of these two centres, the original idea formu-lated by H. H. Meyer in 1913 has been very largely borne out.

One of the problems with the early heating and cooling experiments was that they caused changes in brain temperature of several degrees, while in the normal life of the animal body temperature seldom varied by more than 1–1·5 K. Even when methods were developed for altering the temperature of the hypothalamus alone (by means of implanted thermodes), it was some time before it could be shown experimentally that temperature changes of the order that could be expected in real life were also effective in triggering or inhibiting the various thermoregulatory effectors. The delay was the result of the crudity of the early attempts, coupled with the fact that most of the

151

experiments had to be conducted on animals under general surgical anaesthesia, a procedure which very markedly affects thermoregulatory performance. Most often the body temperature falls as a result of the anaesthetic, and even if it is brought back to normal by external heating, the sensitivity of the central receptors is greatly reduced in that the effector responses occur only after gross changes of temperature.

These problems were solved by the development of surgical techniques which allowed the implantation of thermodes and temperature-measuring devices into the brain under full surgical anaesthesia, but from which the animal was allowed to recover and regain perfectly normal health. Such methods are now so common that they are hardly mentioned in scientific papers, although the resultant ability to perform ' chronic ' experiments on suitably prepared animals has revolutionized the physiology of temperature regulation. Perhaps we should say at this point that, while the passage of steel tubes and pieces of wire through the brain tissue must obviously cause local damage, this is only rarely at the expense of any detectable change in the behaviour or physiology of the animal. Any abnormality resulting from a surgical preparation of this sort would, however, preclude the use of the animal in experiments. The reason for the success of these methods appears to be that certain areas of the brain incorporate a great deal of functional redundancy, in that the operations normally carried out by one structure can often be performed equally well by a duplicate structure, say, on the other side. There is now such confidence in the surgical procedures, that various devices are sometimes inserted into the human brain for therapeutic purposes, and it has been known for many years that quite massive accidental damage to brain tissue may be correlated with little or no recognizable change in function. These generalities must not, of course, be taken too far. They apply most accurately to the cortex of the brain, about which we still understand so little ; substantial damage to the phylogenetically older brain areas, such as the hypothalamus or medulla, may have devastating consequences.

To return to the sensitivity of the hypothalamic thermal receptors, we do now know that changes of the order of 0·2–0·3 K can produce measurable thermoregulatory responses, a sensitivity which would seem adequate for effective control. A strange phenomenon in this connexion, however, is that whereas temperature changes of this magnitude can be shown to elicit normal regulatory responses under experimental conditions, unrestrained animals in which hypothalamic temperature is monitored continuously often exhibit fluctuations a good deal larger, yet without the activation of effector mechanisms. In the domestic fowl, for example, there is a clear relationship between the state of behavioural arousal and the level of hypothalamic temperature (fig. 6.5). When the bird is stimulated in almost any way, the temperature increases rapidly, and when allowed to remain un-disturbed, especially in the dark, it declines to a level almost a full degree below the temperature in the colon. Similar wide fluctuations

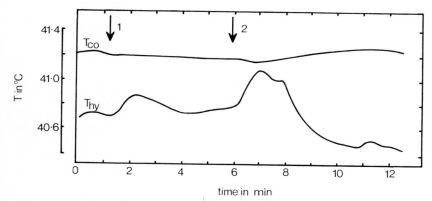

Fig. 6.5. The effect of behavioural arousal on hypothalamic temperature (T_{hy}) in the fowl. 1. Hammering on the wall of the chamber containing the bird caused mild excitement and was accompanied by a rise in hypo-thalamic temperature but no change in the colonic temperature. 2. Opening the chamber door and hammering caused great excitement and a larger rise in hypothalamic temperature. The bird calmed down about 2 min after the door was closed. Hypothalamic temperature then fell sharply while colonic temperature increased as a result of the excite-ment. (Modified from Richards, *J. Physiol.*, 1970.)

in hypothalamic temperature have been observed in several mammals, and they are difficult to reconcile with the apparent high sensitivity of the hypothalamic receptors in initiating thermoregulatory effector responses.

The explanation of this may not prove so elusive as was at first thought. There is increasing evidence that temperature receptors exist in parts of the central nervous system other than the hypothalamus, and even in various parts of the body core outside the central nervous system altogether. If, as is widely believed, the hypothalamus functions as an integrating centre for temperature regulation in addition to its role in temperature-sensitivity, it must be presumed that the hypothalamic neurons are capable of assessing the significance of changes in any given set of central or peripheral receptors in relation to similar, or opposite, changes in other groups of receptors. Thus we might under-stand how local changes in hypothalamic blood flow or local tissue heat production could be overruled by the integrating centres as of no consequence to thermal homoiostasis if, say, skin temperature and the temperature of the body tissues as a whole remained unchanged. When we consider that the hypothalamus is concerned in the control of countless mechanisms involving the autonomic nervous system, the subtle handling of information implied by this explanation cannot be more than we are prepared to believe.

Such has been the interest in the hypothalamic thermal receptors during the last decade or so that the presence of receptors in other parts of the body has been relatively little studied, and even occasionally denied. There is now, however, a good body of evidence that such receptors do exist, and that they play a far more important role in thermoregulation than has hitherto been realized. So far as the central nervous system is concerned there have been scattered reports that the medulla is heat-sensitive, and it has recently been shown that heating and cooling of this area influence behavioural thermoregulation in the rat. By far the most convincing work has been that designed to demonstrate the importance of the temperature of the spinal cord in the dog. The results indicate quite clearly that both the hypothalamus and the spinal cord function as sites for the reception of temperature changes in the body core, and that the effects of such changes on the two are additive. That is, if they are altered simultaneously in the same direction, the influence on responses like shivering or panting is more than that given by the same change in one only. Furthermore, warming one site combined with cooling of the other often results in cancellation of effects. In all important respects, the thermal receptors in the hypothalamus and spinal cord of the dog appear to be very similar.

Deep-body thermal receptors outside the central nervous system have been indicated by several different experimental approaches, but there still remains little definite information as to their precise anatomical location. In the sheep the vena cava and possibly the rumen appear to be temperature-sensitive, in that local cooling and heating both influence thermoregulatory effector mechanisms. There is also evidence for receptors in the femoral vein in the leg of the cat, and also in man, where femoral temperature influences the sweating response. In the anaesthetized fowl, differential heating of the head and body showed that a normal, or slightly sub-normal, temperature at either the hypothalamus or the colon would inhibit the panting response when the temperature of the alternative site was raised to 45–46°C (fig. 6.6). Essentially the same result was achieved when conscious chickens had the temperature of their brains alone raised by up to $3 \cdot 5$ K above normal, so that the initiation of panting appears to require an increase in some temperature outside the head, as well as in that of the hypothalamus.

By now it will be obvious that by far the greatest part of the evidence in favour of central thermal receptors has come from experiments involving local changes in temperature and from observations on the responses of the effector mechanisms which tend to drive body temperature in the opposite direction. An alternative approach is to examine the response characteristics of the receptor cells themselves, in terms of

154

their discharge of electrical impulses, by the technique of 'single unit' recording, similar to that which we encountered with the peripheral receptors.

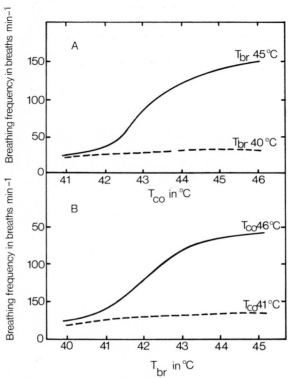

Fig. 6.6. The influence of brain (hypothalamic) temperature and extra-cranial core (colonic) temperature on breathing frequency in the fowl. A. Raising the colonic temperature at a constant hypothalamic temperature of 45°C soon caused panting; at a hypothalamic temperature of 40°C there was no panting. B. Raising the hypothalamic temperature at a constant colonic temperature of 46°C soon caused panting; at 41°C there was none. (Based on data from Richards, *J. Physiol.*, 1970.)

One of the best of such investigations was performed by R. F. Hellon at the National Institute for Medical Research in London. Working on the hypothalamus of the conscious rabbit, he found that all of the single receptor cells which he explored with micro-electrodes showed spontaneous discharging activity, but only about 10 per cent of the cells (27 in number) responded to changes of hypothalamic temperature of the order of plus or minus 2°C. Of these, 21 cells were warmth-sensitive in that they increased their rate of impulse discharge with a rise in

155

temperature and were inhibited by a fall, whereas 6 cells were cold-sensitive in that they responded in the opposite way. Hellon distinguished four separate types of cell, according to the pattern of response that they showed. His type A cells discharged impulses at a frequency that was always directly proportional to their own temperature; type B cells altered their rates of discharge during

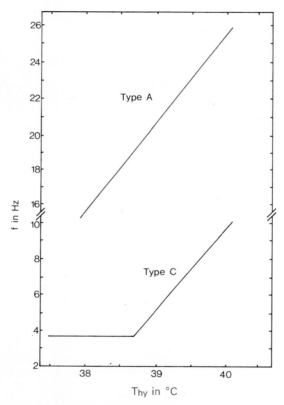

Fig. 6.7. The relation between the frequency of electrical impulses and local temperature in two types of temperature-sensitive neurons of the rabbit's hypothalamus. (Based on data from Hellon, *J. Physiol.*, 1967.)

temperature changes, but their sensitivity to temperature was not affected; type C cells exhibited a sharp temperature threshold, and were influenced only by changes above the threshold (warmth-sensitive) or below (cold-sensitive); finally, type D cells showed changes in discharge frequencies which either led or lagged behind the alterations in temperature. The type A and C cells are the most interesting so far

156

as temperature regulation is concerned (fig. 6.7), and we shall see below that the discharge characteristics of these cells in the rabbit coincide very nicely with some of the fundamental features of the thermo-regulatory mechanisms in man.

Further work on the rabbit has now shown that heating and cooling of the spinal cord can also cause discharges of hypothalamic neurones, sometimes in a manner which is additive with respect to the effects of local hypothalamic heating. In the cat there are neurons in the spinal cord itself which have been shown to discharge at a rate that is pro-portional to the temperature of the vertebral canal, while in either case the effects of spinal heating and cooling appear to be transmitted to the hypothalamus by way of the ventro-lateral nerve tracts in the cord. Thus the electrophysiological studies have broadly supported the earlier ones which utilized the stimulation of effector mechanisms, and confirm beyond doubt that thermal receptors exist in the central nervous system outside the hypothalamus as well as within it.

6.4. NERVOUS INTEGRATION

6.4.1. The Theory of Control Systems

A good deal of insight into the workings of biological regulating systems has been gained by comparison of their components with the physical control systems used by engineers. We have seen on many occasions that the core temperature of birds and mammals is maintained relatively constant, while the peripheral tissues that we call the shell are allowed to fluctuate widely according to ambient conditions. In a physical system of comparable thermal distribution, an engineer would require a 'set-point' or reference temperature and a temperature-sensing element situated deep in the central mass. The actual tem-perature of the mass would then be continuously compared by the receptor with the set-point, the discrepancy between the two being known as the load error. The responses of the thermoregulatory effector mechanisms would then be related in one of several possible ways to this load error, such that the temperature of the central mass would fluctuate somewhat on either side of the set-point. The characteristics of these fluctuations would be a measure of the sensitivity of the regulating system. The sensitivity could be enhanced, and the fluctua-tions reduced, by adding peripheral thermal receptors able to initiate anticipatory responses which might occur in some instances without any change in the central temperature.

Three types of control system used by engineers can be identified with analogous physiological situations. The simplest is the 'on–off' controller, familiar as the usual domestic thermostat. This shows an all-or-nothing response, in that it switches a cooling or heating device in or out of action as the temperature being regulated oscillates above or below the set-point. There are numerous physiological examples, including the responses of a lizard in seeking shade at a fixed level of body temperature, or the panting of a dog which tends to be turned on and off abruptly as the body warms or cools beyond the threshold temperature.

A defect of the simple on–off controller is that there are typically considerable fluctuations of the temperature because of the thermal inertia of the system. A more stable system is achieved by the continuous proportional or 'throttling' controller, in which there is a linear relation between the load error and the magnitude of the effector action. A bimetallic temperature detector actuating a rheostat which governs the amount of heating necessary to control the temperature of a water bath would be a simple physical example. In physiology there appear to be many examples, one of which is the sweating response in man, which varies in intensity directly with the elevation of central temperature above the set-point.

The third type of system uses the rate controller, which acts by quickening the effector response according to the rate of change of the load error, rather than the error itself. This sort of controller will not keep temperature at a fixed level because the effector is responsive solely to rate ; that is, it will only stabilize the temperature at a new level. In practice, the rate controller is therefore usually combined with proportional control. In the body the two appear to be combined during the adjustments of core temperature that occur in fever.

All of these systems employ what are called 'feedback' effects, by which the final effector responses in some way influence the input to the system. The concept of feedback is fundamental to all homoiostatic mechanisms, and it is readily illustrated by the simple example of the control of the temperature of a room (fig. 6.8). If we wish to maintain the room temperature constant all the year round it will be necessary to have available means for both heating and cooling the room air (the effectors), together with a thermostat which activates either the source of warm air or that of cool air according to the direction in which the room temperature fluctuates from the set-point. The feedback in this system would be the room temperature prevailing at a given moment, which the thermostat (the detector) would compare with the set-point. When a deviation from the set-point starts off mechanisms which tend to restore the original situation, the feedback is said to be negative ; by definition, it is therefore negative feedback which operates in homoiostasis. This is further illustrated in fig. 6.9 in terms of the various elements in the control system for body temperature.

If the mechanisms that are set in motion by a deviation from the set-point have the effect of increasing the deviation further, the feedback is said to be positive. This is a rare thing in physiology, although we have, in fact, already encountered an example in connexion with the thermal receptors of the skin. Application of cold to the skin causes local vasoconstriction which further reduces the temperature, enhances the sensation of cold, and accelerates the discharge frequency of the receptors. Such positive feedback in the skin may serve the purpose of providing a rapid emergency response which permits the avoidance of dangerous thermal situations by behaviour, yet does not upset the core temperature because of the restriction of its effect to the shell.

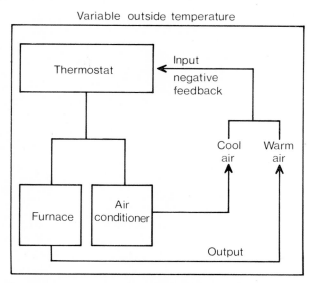

Fig. 6.8. Diagram illustrating the principle of feedback in terms of the control of room temperature.

There is still a good deal of controversy about the applicability of control theory to physiological and behavioural temperature regulation, but there is no longer a major dispute about the importance of the hypothalamus, both as a site for central thermal detection and as the primary centre for integration of thermal information. There is now a great deal of support for the idea that the set-point of the physiological thermostat is not fixed, but is a variable function of a host of factors including central temperature, peripheral temperature, and a variety of sensory stimuli not necessarily connected in any obvious way with temperature regulation. The thermoregulatory effector responses are initiated as a result of the load error, but this may change in accordance with alterations in the set-point, perhaps without any change in hypothalamic temperature. On the other hand, if a change in hypothalamic temperature were balanced by a simultaneous change in the set-point,

159

then there need be no change in the load error. A simple sketch of the hypothesis is given in fig. 6.10.

Close control of body temperature around this set-point appears to explain normal thermoregulation as it can be observed in mammals and birds, even though it almost certainly evolved separately in the two classes. Recently, J. Bligh has put forward some interesting evidence which suggests a more primitive, secondary level of thermoregulation, possibly inherited jointly by both classes, and which now serves only to

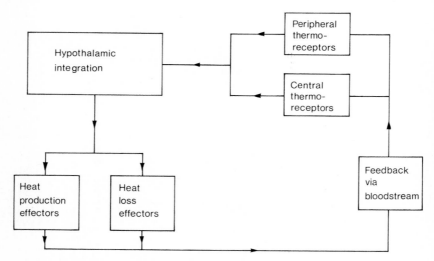

Fig. 6.9. Diagram illustrating the control of body temperature. The hypothalamus receives information on the body's thermal state from both central and peripheral receptors. It initiates the necessary reactions to maintain constancy of temperature by its controlling influence on the neural and hormonal effector mechanisms. Information on the results of these reactions is then fed back to the receptors by way of the circulating blood.

protect the organism against disastrous deviations in core temperature under abnormal conditions (fig. 6.11). The idea was suggested to Bligh by the observation that there appear to be definite limits to temperature fluctuations in mammals, even after the close control around the set-point has broken down in fever, for instance, or during surgical anaesthesia. The critical upper and lower limits in mammals are at about 40·5–41°C and 35–36°C, and the preliminary indications are that this ' broad band ' control operates quite independently of the normal regulatory mechanisms. It may be dependent solely upon hypothalamic thermosensitivity, which we have seen to be present in all classes of vertebrates, and may operate by a simple on–off controller.

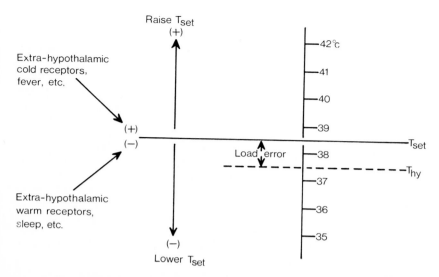

Fig. 6.10. Diagram illustrating the idea of the variable set-point temperature (T_{set}). Thermoregulatory responses are controlled by and proportional to the load error (difference between T_{set} and the prevailing T_{hy}). When $T_{hy} > T_{set}$, sweating or panting and peripheral vasodilatation occur ; when $T_{hy} < T_{set}$ there is shivering and vasoconstriction. However, T_{set} is itself variable as a result of afferent nervous influences from temperature receptors outside the hypothalamus, as well as from receptors associated with other factors such as fever, exercise, sleep and pain. (Based on Bligh, *Biol. Rev.*, 1966.)

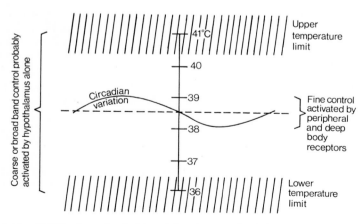

Fig. 6.11. Bligh's hypothetical two-tiered control of deep body temperature. (Based on Bligh, *Biol. Rev.*, 1966.)

161

While it is too early yet to evaluate this idea more fully, it has great interest both in the phylogenetic sense and as an explanation of the control of body temperature seen in some animals under extreme situations (Chapter 7).

6.4.2. *Thermal Homoiostasis in Man : an Example of Nervous Integration*

In a recent review article, T. H. Benzinger has brought together an enormous quantity of information from the physiological literature which illustrates many of the principles that we have been discussing. While there is still disagreement on some minor aspects of Benzinger's views and interpretations, the bulk of his thesis is now accepted by most physiologists, and we cannot do better than consider briefly the main conclusions and the experimental evidence upon which they are based.

Benzinger's own experimental results, which form the basis of his article, are heavily dependent upon the two techniques of gradient-layer calorimetry and tympanic membrane thermometry. These were developed very largely by his team at the Naval Medical Research Institute in Bethesda, Maryland, working on subjects who included a number of well known American astronauts. As we have seen, the gradient-layer calorimeter (see fig. 3.4) is especially valuable for following rapid changes of heat loss from the body, while the use of the eardrum as the site for monitoring the deep body temperature in man has proved particularly valuable for the speed of its response (compared, say, to that of rectal temperature) and for being the closest approximation to hypothalamic temperature. Indeed, many of Benzinger's results could not be demonstrated if rectal temperature were used instead of tympanic, largely because of the thermal lag which always occurs in the rectum under rapidly changing conditions.

One final thing that we need to know about Benzinger's approach is that many of his experiments involve the use of water baths at various temperatures into which the experimental subjects may be lowered passively (i.e. without muscular exertion) in order to obtain any particular combination of cranial (tympanic) temperature and skin temperature. Dissociation of the two is necessary if their respective roles in controlling the effector responses are to be distinguished.

6.4.2.1. *Chemical thermoregulation*

If a subject, resting naked in cool air (12°C), consumes 450 g of ice, there is a fall in tympanic temperature of about 0·5 K and a violent rise in metabolic rate to about three times the resting level (fig. 6.12 A). On first acquaintance this response appears to be the result of the central reception of cold by the brain, but another experiment shows that a more subtle explanation is the correct one. The subject first has his core temperature lowered somewhat below normal by immersion of all except the head in a cool bath. When his tympanic temperature

162

has descended to about 36°C he is allowed to rest in a comfortable bath at 37°C. A brief exposure to another cool bath (28°C) is now seen to result in a dramatic increase in metabolism which coincides precisely with the sudden decrease in skin (bath) temperature (fig. 6.12 B).

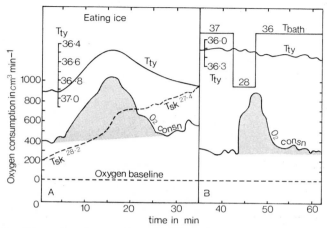

Fig. 6.12. The role of central temperature (tympanic, T_{ty}) and peripheral (skin) temperature in regulating the rate of heat production (oxygen consumption) in man. Note the inverted temperature scales. (Redrawn and modified from Benzinger, *Physiol. Rev.*, 1969.)

Thus, in this experiment the rise in metabolism appears to be due to the fall in peripheral temperature. Careful analysis has shown that the same explanation also applied to the first; the rise of heat production resulted, not from the fall in central temperature, but from the persistent cold-reception at the skin (in the 12°C environment) which was temporarily released from central warm-inhibition. Similarly, the response seen in the second experiment fails to occur if the central temperature is not first lowered below normal.

The correctness of this explanation of chemical regulation in man is shown most elegantly by a long series of experiments in which the metabolic rate of a single subject was plotted against a wide range of both tympanic and skin temperature, obtained by pre-heating and pre-cooling in appropriate water baths. By these procedures, the central temperature range was varied between 36 and 38°C, and the skin temperature between 12 and 37°C. The principal results are shown in figs. 6.13 and 6.14, which represent 'tympanic isotherms' (all metabolic measurements made at equal tympanic temperatures were connected) and 'skin isotherms' (measurements at equal skin temperatures) respectively. Figure 6.13 shows that the maximum metabolic response

163

occurs at a skin temperature of about 20°C and declines somewhat on either side. There is no metabolic response, however, even at 20°C skin temperature, if the central temperature in this subject is higher

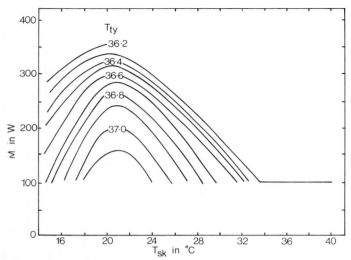

Fig. 6.13. Metabolic heat production in man is controlled by peripheral cold-excitation and central warm-inhibition. (Redrawn and modified from Benzinger, *Physiol. Rev.*, 1969.)

than 37·1°C; the peripheral cold-induced response is inhibited completely by this level of central temperature and the response is gradually released from warmth-inhibition as the central temperature falls from 37 to 36°C. Likewise in fig. 6.14, if we view the graph from right to left, we see that there is no metabolic response, even at a skin temperature of 20°C, until the central temperature has declined below 37·1°C. The reaction then increases in relation to the falling central inhibition and the increasing peripheral stimulation.

This explanation of the cold-induced metabolic response in man as being the result of peripheral cold-excitation and central warmth-inhibition is summarized diagrammatically in fig. 6.15. The centre chiefly concerned in chemical regulation is that in the posterior hypothalamus (P). If this centre (in animals) is destroyed experimentally, chemical regulation is abolished. However, the centre in man appears to be 'temperature-blind', for it does not drive the metabolic response directly as a result of central cooling but functions as a relay centre for transmitting afferent impulses from cold-receptors in the skin. The anterior hypothalamic centre (A) is temperature-sensitive, and central reception of warmth at this point has an inhibitory effect on P.

Although the normal metabolic response to cold in man occurs as a result of peripheral stimulation, and is not due to direct temperature-sensitivity in the brain, central cold-reception nevertheless does occur. This had been shown in experiments on patients suffering from complete section of the cervical spinal cord, where the transmission to the brain of cold stimuli from the greater part of the skin is impossible.

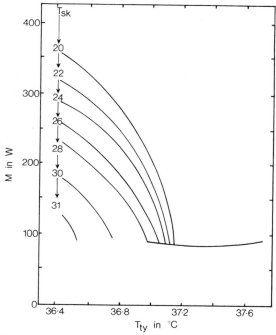

Fig. 6.14. The same metabolic data as those of fig. 6.13 plotted against tympanic temperature. (Redrawn and modified from Benzinger, *Physiol. Rev.*, 1969.)

Despite this severe and permanent injury, it has been found that a weak metabolic response to cold does occur when central cooling is carried below about 35·7°C, that is, beyond the range of normal thermal homoiostasis. The maximum rate of heat production resulting from this degree of central cooling is, however, only about 5 per cent of that due to peripheral cooling in normal subjects (see table 6). This second, weaker mechanism of triggering the metabolic response is not normally operational in intact man, for the sensitivity of the peripheral mechanism is much greater and its set-point is much higher. Therefore, the weaker mechanism gets no chance to function under natural conditions, although it may have a role to play in unnatural extremes, such as would

165

be required by Bligh's secondary broad-band type of thermoregulation.

A third mechanism concerned with chemical regulation is that based on cold-reception in the spinal cord. We need not dwell on this, however, because in man the mechanism appears to be far weaker even than

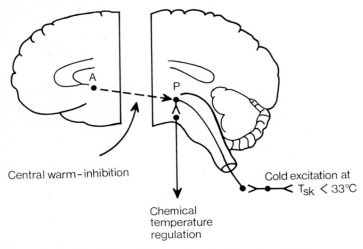

Fig. 6.15. Diagram of the brain centres involved in chemical thermoregulation in man. (Redrawn from Benzinger, *Physiol. Rev.*, 1969.)

that due to cerebral cold-reception, and it could not function under normal circumstances for the same reasons as have been outlined above.

6.4.2.2. *Behavioural regulation against cold*

Chemical regulation is expensive, and for this reason can be sustained at high levels only for short periods. In any case, the maximum response occurs only at a skin temperature of 20°C ; if the skin temperature has not fallen that far then the response is weaker, and even then it comes too late, for the central temperature must already have declined. This is probably why chemical regulation is normally combined with cold-avoiding behaviour. Indeed, under the great majority of conditions, the behavioural response to cold is by far the most important, and the experimental approach has revealed an interesting difference between the mechanism controlling the metabolic response on the one hand and that controlling the behavioural (conscious) response on the other.

A subject is immersed up to the head in a water bath at 38°C after various pre-conditioning procedures with warm and cool baths to influence his central temperature. The temperature of the 38°C bath is arranged to decline at a rate of 1 K h^{-1}, and the subject is asked to report his first distinguishable sensation of coolness. Typical results are shown in fig. 6.16, in which the lower curve represents the metabolic response (explained in the legend) for the same subject. Over the range of

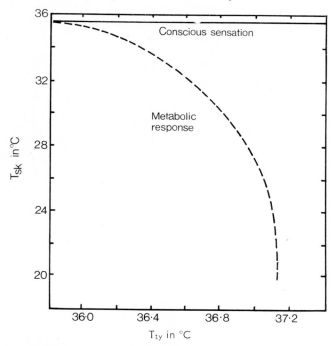

Fig. 6.16. Threshold combinations of skin temperature and tympanic temperature for the conscious sensation of cold and for the metabolic response to cold. The sensation of cold is not affected by central temperature, while the metabolic response is subject to central warmth inhibition. At the top of the graph there is no central inhibiting effect and the thresholds for the two reactions are equal. The curve of metabolic response depicts the combination of temperatures at which metabolism rose just above basal. At a tympanic temperature of 37·1 °C, central warmth-inhibition was total, so that there was no metabolic response, even at 20°C skin temperature. (Redrawn and modified from Benzinger, *Physiol. Rev.*, 1969.)

temperatures investigated, no evidence could be found of a central contribution to the conscious sensation of cold, either of cold excitation or of warmth-inhibition. This contrasted dramatically with the central warmth-inhibition of the metabolic response to peripheral cold, and the distinction implies that there must be two separate sets of cold-receptors in the skin, connected to separate effector systems, one for the metabolic reaction which is subject to warmth-inhibition centrally, and the other

167

for the conscious sensation of cold which cannot be influenced by central factors.

The vital importance of the behavioural system in man lies in its ability to act as an early-warning device which can elicit appropriate behavioural action regardless of the state of central temperature and long before this is reduced by the influence of cold. Following the

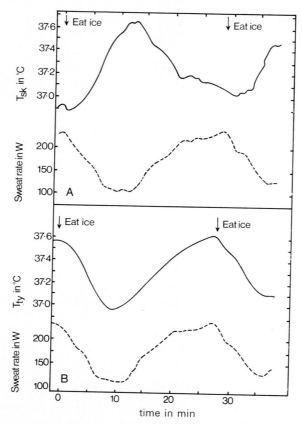

Fig. 6.17. The relationship of rate of sweating (shown as rate of loss of energy by evaporation) to skin temperature and tympanic temperature. (Re-drawn and modified from Benzinger, *Physiol. Rev.*, 1969.)

discovery of the weak central cold-receptors on the metabolic side, we cannot at this stage rule out the possibility that a secondary central conscious sensation of cold also exists at a lower range of body temperature than has so far been investigated.

168

6.4.2.3. *Physical thermoregulation*

The first important result which emerged from the use of gradient-layer calorimetry and tympanic thermometry in the study of thermal sweating activity in man was that skin temperature and rate of sweating

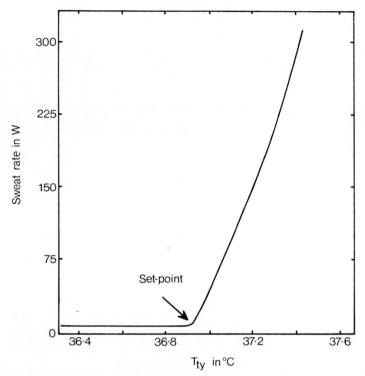

Fig. 6.18. The relationship between rate of sweating and tympanic temperature. The curve represents the mean of values obtained at rest and during exercise at a wide variety of skin temperatures. (Redrawn and modified from Benzinger, *Physiol. Rev.*, 1969.)

always moved in opposite directions. For example, a subject working in a warm environment would always have a relatively low skin temperature and a high rate of sweating so long as he continued to work. With the cessation of activity, his skin temperature would rise and the rate of sweating fall. Further, if the subject lowered his central temperature by eating ice, this raised the skin temperature and reduced the sweating rate simultaneously (fig. 6.17 A). These experiments at first appeared paradoxical in that cooling of the skin seemed to excite the sweat glands, but in reality the relation observed between skin temperature and sweating rate was of a physical rather than a physiological nature. That

M   169

is, it was the evaporation of sweat on the skin that caused the skin temperature to fall.

Opposite results were obtained when the rate of sweating was compared with central temperature. Under all circumstances the patterns of the two parameters were concordant. Thus, exercise in a warm environment caused a rise in central temperature and a concurrent rise in sweating rate ; the ingestion of ice to cause central cooling also caused a fall in the rate of sweating (fig. 6.17 B). It appeared that central warmth-reception and not peripheral warmth-reception was the stimulus for sweating.

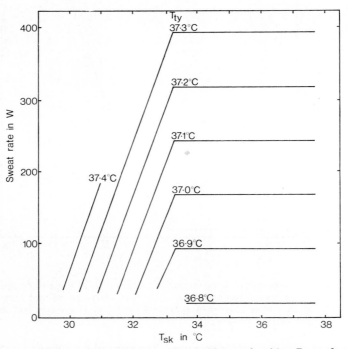

Fig. 6.19. Inhibition of sweating by cold-reception at the skin. Rate of sweating is independent of skin temperature in the warm range (tympanic isotherms parallel to abscissae). Below 33°C however, there is increasing inhibition (slanting isotherms). (Redrawn and modified from Benzinger, *Physiol. Rev.*, 1969.)

When the sweating response was plotted against the temperature of the skin, no consistent relationship could be demonstrated. Plotted against central temperature, however, there was the most striking linear relation shown in fig. 6.18 ; this should be compared with

170

figs. 6.13 and 6.14. The most important characteristics of the relationship were the start of the sweating response at a sharply determined threshold temperature (the set-point), below which there was no response, and the direct proportionality between the effector response and the load error. This was one of the first direct pieces of evidence for the human thermostat.

The sensitivity of the sweating response is remarkable. The steady-state rate of heat loss is increased by about 10 per cent of the basal metabolic rate for every $0 \cdot 01$ K rise in the load error. Put another way, the system can cope with a heat load of four basal metabolic rates for a load error of only $0 \cdot 5$ K. Despite its sensitivity, however, the centrally-induced sweating reaction may be inhibited by cold-reception at the skin. This effect is familiar to anyone who has exercised vigorously on a really cold day. The intensity of the inhibition is also remarkable. If expressed as the relation between the depression of the sweating response and the peripheral cold stimulus, it is about two basal metabolic rates for each degree, which is ten times as sensitive as the elicitation of metabolic heat production by skin cold-reception of the same intensity (see table 6). An experiment illustrating the effect is summarized in fig. 6.19. In this subject, the rate of sweating was progressively reduced with falling skin temperature below 33°C. The inhibition of sweating under such conditions may be regarded as ' anti-homoiostatic ' because during strenuous exercise the central temperature will rise above the normal level. Its value appears to be in preventing sweating in cool environments when the moisture could not evaporate. A wet skin would not only be uncomfortable, but also potentially dangerous in the cold during the recovery period after exercise. The latter is, in any case, always of short duration.

6.4.2.4. *Behavioural regulation against warmth*

The sensation of warmth on the skin is pleasant. The disagreeable sensation of being over-heated is usually recognized as being internal, not peripheral, as can be shown by immersing a subject in a water bath at 38°C. Provided that on entry to the bath his central temperature is normal or below normal, the subject does not report discomfort for some minutes, despite the fact that his skin temperature is several degrees higher than its usual level. Only when the central temperature is raised does the alarming sensation of over-heating become conscious. This implies a serious weakness in the behavioural reaction to heat, for the autonomic defences will be maximally operational long before a serious situation is detected, which may explain the cases where athletes in hot climates have died from hyperthermia.

In this respect you will notice that the conscious sensation of warmth tends to be the opposite to that of cold. In fact we might say that in man the behavioural response against cold and the physiological

171

response against heat are the dominant factors, while the behavioural response to heat and the physiological response to cold are much weaker and much less effective. The conscious sensation of cold elicits reactions that drive the central body temperature upwards to the level of the set-point and beyond ; that is, the set-point of man's thermostat is approached from below by behaviour. By contrast, the return to the set-point from above is achieved, not by behaviour, but by the autonomic response of sweating (and by vasodilatation, which appears to be controlled in a manner similar to sweating).

6.4.2.5. *Thermal receptors and temperature regulation in man*

If the discharge characteristics of the peripheral and central temperature receptors could be shown to be related in some obvious way to the patterns of heat production and heat loss seen in the experiments described above, we should have a strong basis of support for the interpretations given. The great majority of work on thermal receptors has been performed on animals, and we have therefore to make extrapolations from one species to another. This of course is an unfortunate weakness in the approach, but it is nevertheless worth summarizing briefly what information we have.

The discharge of electrical impulses by the cold-receptors of the cat's tongue form a pattern, when plotted against tongue temperature, that is very similar to that of oxygen consumption in man plotted against skin temperature (compare figs. 6.4 and 6.13). Furthermore, there is evidence that the maximum frequency of discharge of impulses in the cold-receptors of human skin occurs at about 20°C, just as does the maximum metabolic response. The inhibition of the peripherally-induced metabolic response by central warmth appears to be explicable in terms of Hellon's type A neurons, for they begin to discharge impulses at temperatures well below the set-point at which the warmth-sensitive neurons begin to discharge. The latter seem to be well represented by Hellon's type C cells, which coincide in pattern of activity very strikingly with the pattern of the sweating response in man (compare figs. 6.7 and 6.18). The neurons are characterized by a set-point below which no increase in discharge frequency occurs, and by a direct proportionality between frequency and temperature increment above the set-point. Finally, it is possible that the cold-sensitive type B cells of Hellon are responsible for the weak, central elicitation of shivering in patients with section of the spinal cord.

Table 6 summarizes this information on receptor function and relates it tentatively to the picture that we have built up of the mechanisms that regulate body temperature in man. In the first column of the table the heat-producing or heat-dissipating capacities of the various physiological mechanisms are assessed in multiples of basal metabolic rate per unit change of central or peripheral temperature. The second

172

column considers the sensitivity of the respective receptor sites in terms of the frequency of discharge of nervous impulses elicited per second and per unit change of temperature. The third column illustrates the sensitivity of the effector systems (again in terms of multiples of basal metabolic rate) when each one of the neurons concerned discharges,

	Heat loss or production in BMR K^{-1}	Receptor sensitivity in impulses $s^{-1} K^{-1}$	Effector sensitivity in BMR impulse^{-1}
Main central mechanisms			
Sweating (cerebral warm-excitation)	$-10\cdot0$	10	$-1\cdot0$
Shivering (release from cerebral warm-inhibition)	$+10\cdot0$	5	$+2\cdot0$
Weak central mechanisms			
Shivering (cerebral cold-excitation)	$+0\cdot5$	10	$+0\cdot05$
Shivering (spinal cold-excitation)	$+0\cdot1$	—	—
Peripheral mechanisms			
Shivering (peripheral cold-excitation)	$+0\cdot2$	1	$+0\cdot2$
Sweating (peripheral cold-inhibition)	$+2\cdot0$	1	$+2\cdot0$

Table 6. Nervous mechanisms of human temperature regulation. Modified from Benzinger, *Physiol. Rev.*, 1969. The data on impulses from central receptors are from the rabbit—Hellon, *J. Physiol.*, 1967—because they are unobtainable in man. The hormonal mechanisms of heat production are not included.

on average, one impulse. The preliminary conclusions that may be drawn are as follows : (i) Central neurons are one or two orders of magnitude (i.e. 10 to 100 times) more responsive to temperature than peripheral neurons. (ii) Despite this, central and peripheral mechanisms are comparable in effect because the temperature range available for stimulation is one or two orders of magnitude greater for peripheral than it is for central neurons. (iii) In effector efficiency, the inhibitory mechanisms seem to be superior to excitatory mechanisms. (iv) The mechanisms based on hypothalamic and possibly on spinal cold-receptors are too weak to play other than emergency roles.

6.5. HORMONES, DRUGS AND TEMPERATURE REGULATION

A great deal more information will be required on the role of neurons and synapses in the control of body temperature before we can hope to understand the complex actions of chemical transmitters and drugs.

To be sure, great strides have been made in the last decade, and once again these have come about because it has been possible to investigate the actions of such materials on conscious animals with minute tubes permanently implanted into the brain. It was only the development of this technique that allowed the separation of drug effects into the two possible components, the central and the extra-central or systemic. This was a vital step forward, because what is known as the blood/brain barrier often prevents materials which are injected into the blood stream or body cavity from reaching the brain cells themselves, but it is these cells that are the site of major interest so far as temperature regulation is concerned.

The blood/brain barrier is believed to be a property of the neuroglial cells which surround the capillaries of the central nervous system. The capillaries themselves do not appear to differ from those elsewhere in the body, and yet a number of substances that can pass through the general capillary walls do not do so in the central nervous system. The only way that the effect of these substances can be tested on brain cells directly is therefore by injecting them through implanted cannulae.

The most important current hypothesis of the neuronal or synaptic control of body temperature was developed in this way about ten years ago by W. Feldberg and R. D. Myers at the National Institute for Medical Research. It had been known for some time that the mono-amines adrenaline, noradrenaline and 5-hydroxytryptamine, occur naturally in the hypothalamus, and it was first suggested in 1957 that these substances may be concerned in the regulation of temperature. It was then found that when the amines were injected into the brain ventricles of the cat they did, in fact, bring about changes in the body temperature by means of the usual effector mechanisms. In this species, noradrenaline and adrenaline caused a fall in temperature by inhibiting the shivering response, while 5-hydroxytryptamine caused a rise by stimulating shivering. It was thus proposed that the controlled release of these naturally occurring amines from nerve endings in the hypothalamus was the means whereby the regulation of body temperature was achieved. There is now a good deal of support for this general idea, although subsequent work has shown very wide differences in the responses of various mammalian species.

Some of the most interesting work has been performed by Bligh and his colleagues at the Institute of Animal Physiology near Cambridge. They have used mainly sheep, goats and rabbits, species which happen to show opposite responses to those most often described in the cat, dog and monkey. The fundamental basis of these differences is not yet understood, but they need not affect the validity of the general hypo-thesis. In sheep, goats and rabbits, 5-hydroxytryptamine injected into the brain ventricles caused a fall in body temperature by means of an excitatory effect on the functional pathway involving the reception of the stimulus of warmth and the activation of the mechanisms of heat loss. The way by which the effect was achieved, however, depended on environmental temperature. At high temperature there was an increase in evaporative heat loss, while at low temperature there was a decrease in shivering. The effect of noradrenaline was to reduce evaporative heat loss and cause a rise in body temperature at high environmental temperature, but to reduce shivering and cause a fall in body temperature at low ambient temperature. These effects were interpreted as those of inhibition on both the pathway of warmth reception and heat loss, and on that involving cold-reception and heat production.

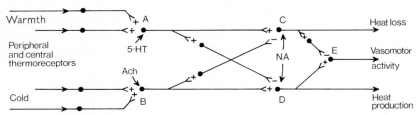

Fig. 6.20. A hypothetical model representing part of the neuronal pathways between warmth receptors and heat-loss effectors and between cold receptors and heat-production effectors, including crossed inhibitory pathways between them. In the sheep, goat and rabbit, 5-hydroxy-tryptamine (5-HT) acts as an excitatory substance at synapse A. Acetylcholine (Ach) is excitatory at synapse B. Noradrenaline (NA) is inhibitory at both synapses C and D. The effects of these substances on peripheral vasomotor activity were of excitation from the heat-production pathway and of inhibition from the heat-loss pathway ; both acted at synapse E. (Based on Bligh *et al.*, *J. Physiol.*, 1971 and Bligh and Maskrey, *J. Physiol.*, 1970.)

Bligh also studied the effects of acetylcholine, the substance liberated by nerve endings of the parasympathetic system. The effects were rather more unpredictable, but appeared in essence to be excitatory on the cold-reception and heat production pathways. The influence of the three substances is summarized in fig. 6.20, which is a preliminary attempt to understand the possible neuronal and synaptic actions of the transmitter substances. The model includes crossed inhibitory pathways in addition to the two main pathways, because heat production is reduced by exposure to heat, and heat loss is reduced by exposure to cold. The model is a useful aid in our attempts to understand the effects of centrally-active substances on thermoregulation, although it does of course represent only part of the intermediate pathways between the receptors and effectors. We have very little knowledge of the physiology of the central control mechanisms, and it looks as if such an understanding may come eventually from studies of the effects of locally administered drugs. Indeed, much of the support for the original monoamine hypothesis of body-temperature regulation has come from investigations with chemical materials that are known to interfere with the synthesis, release and inactivation of the naturally occurring transmitters.

We cannot spend much time in the specialized field of pharmacology, although an example of drug action will give us some idea of the importance of these investigations in the basic attempt to comprehend the workings of the central controller. The effect of anaesthetic drugs is generally to cause a profound disturbance of normal thermoregulation in addition to the other depressant effects on the nervous system. The influence on temperature regulation may not be the result of these general disturbances but appears, rather, to be a local effect on the hypothalamic thermoregulatory mechanisms. If artificial cerebrospinal fluid containing the common anaesthetic chloralose is infused into the brain ventricles of the cat there is a fall in body temperature. This is similar to the effect of noradrenaline in this species. However, if the chloralose infusion is carried out after the hypothalamus has been rendered insensitive to noradrenaline by first injecting the drug ergotamine, then there is no drop in body temperature. The likely explanation for the effect of the anaesthetic is therefore that it stimulates the release of noradrenaline in the hypothalamus.

6.6. DISORDERS OF THE CENTRAL MECHANISMS

6.6.1. Fever

Another example of the action of a group of foreign materials on thermoregulation is that of the pyrogens which are associated with fever (pyrexia). Pyrogens are lipopolysaccharides of high molecular weight which can be isolated from various types of bacteria and viruses; they are also formed by the white cells in the blood in the presence of tissue damage or infection. If they are injected into a peripheral artery there is no local vasoconstriction in that particular vascular bed, and when they are introduced into a patient with a completely severed spinal cord the processes of fever, chiefly manifest as excitation of the heat conservation mechanisms, are observed only in regions innervated from above the spinal damage. This suggests that pyrogens act directly on the hypothalamic neurons, especially as minute amounts injected directly into the hypothalamus of animals cause some of the symptoms of fever, including a raised body temperature. It has therefore been proposed that the pyrogens may function by facilitating or inhibiting the release of noradrenaline or 5-hydroxytryptamine. Some doubt is now cast on this explanation, however, because while there are no specific differences in the response to pyrogens, there are wide differences in the effect of the

176

various amines. The action of pyrogens on the release of amines would therefore have to be different in various animals.

The function of fever, if any, is poorly understood. The central regulating mechanisms appear to operate around a new temperature, so that it is often said that in fever the set-point is raised. The explanation is not known for certain, but the demonstration that pyrogens cause a fall in the content of calcium in the plasma was one of the first indications that the physiological basis of the set-point may be the level of this ion. More recent experiments suggest that the set-point may rather be the result of the ratio between the concentrations of calcium and of sodium ions in the hypothalamus; if the level of one or other ion is altered there is a marked change in core temperature, but if both are altered simultaneously in the same ratio there is no change. Since these ions are known to have a profound influence on nervous activity, it is postulated that their ratio determines the discharge characteristics of the neurons concerned in temperature regulation.

The rise in body temperature during fever is the result of a reduction in the activity of the mechanisms for heat loss and possibly of an increase in heat production, but as yet there is only limited evidence of an acceleration of the body's defence reactions to overcome the processes of disease. One of the most interesting aspects is that once the new level of temperature has been attained the thermoregulatory processes seem to function fairly normally. For example, in man, despite a hyperthermia of 2–3 K induced by fever, there is usually no sweating, since the new temperature is still below the raised set-point for that response. If the body temperature is artificially lowered to normal, shivering commences together with a further enhancement of the mechanisms of heat conservation. However, it must be assumed that the pyrogens do weaken the body's thermoregulatory powers since otherwise the raised temperature would presumably be counteracted in the normal way.

6.6.2. *Hyperthermia in Surgery*

As we have seen, the common response to anaesthetic drugs is a fall in the body temperature. In the last few years, however, another reaction has been recognized, that now called 'fulminant hyperthermia'. The explanation of this syndrome is as yet completely unknown, although it is much more serious than fever since it involves excessive heat production and at the present time is frequently fatal. It has been observed in patients undergoing routine surgical and anaesthetic procedures and proneness to the syndrome appears to be hereditary. The only possible remedy is any emergency action that may help to reduce the high temperature.

177

CHAPTER 7
animals and climate

THE concept of homoiostasis is important in physiology because the external environment does vary. If it never changed, all animals might be expected to establish an internal equilibrium with the external conditions and thereby gain an automatic stability. This may be more or less what happens in some deep and sheltered aquatic habitats, but on land there is always a degree of variation, at least according to season or during some phase of an animal's life cycle.

Important among the continuously changing conditions experienced by most animals are the factors that we call climatic, including such phenomena as ambient and radiant temperature, humidity and air movement. In addition there are factors such as light, sounds, odours, various sorts of radiation, the availability of food and the presence or absence of other animals, which are not primarily climatic although they may be influenced by climate. The climatic factors are those which have the principal thermal impact on animals and they are therefore the ones of chief interest in connexion with temperature regulation.

7.1. *THE THERMAL ENVIRONMENT*

The environmental parameters measured by the meteorologist, such as air temperature and pressure, or precipitation, all have effects of thermal significance. The sum total of these factors constitute what we understand by the term weather, and the average weather of a given region is described as its climate. The climate of the meteorologist may, however, be very different from that experienced by an animal in the same general location, so that we distinguish between the macroclimate of the total atmosphere above whole regions, and the microclimate of the immediate surroundings of an organism. A further sub-division, the mesoclimate, is sometimes used to distinguish a modification of the macroclimate produced by a natural or artificial shelter, such as a hill or wind-break, on the lee side of which there may be substantial differences from the exposed side.

An animal's microclimate is influenced, and even controlled to some extent, by the animal itself through its behaviour. This seems to be modified so as to achieve optimum conditions of comfort around the animal by means of altering the exchange of heat between the body and its surroundings. Thus, conductive heat transfer will be influenced by

178

the degree of contact with the substratum, radiant exchange by the animal's posture and shade-seeking behaviour, convective and evaporative transfer by local conditions of humidity, temperature and air movement, which themselves may be influenced by shelter from wind and rain. The microclimate that is achieved is therefore the immediately effective climate of the animal.

A final category of climate that is sometimes distinguished is that known as the cryptoclimate within a house, burrow or cave. We have seen that the shelters provided by man for himself are a special case of his behavioural response to hostile climate, but it is interesting that in recent years he has increasingly provided similar protection for the animals that he husbands. Thus the conditions experienced by many domestic animals are now those of the cryptoclimate inside the buildings

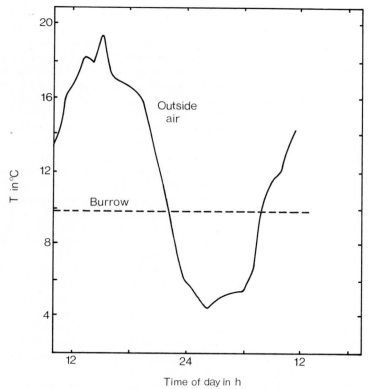

Time of day in h

Fig. 7.1. The thermal constancy provided by the burrow of the deermouse (*Peromyscus maniculatus*) during diurnal fluctuations of the outside temperature. (Redrawn and modified by permission of the National Research Council of Canada from Hayward, *Can. J. Zool.*, **43**, pp. 341–350, 1965.)

used for intensive rearing and production. Even this, however, is an over-simplification, for the microclimate of the intensively housed animal is greatly influenced by the proximity of its fellow creatures, a consideration which may have vital importance during severe fluctuations in the macroclimate.

In nature, the cryptoclimate provided by a burrow is often the chief factor permitting survival in a macroclimate that would be too demanding of the thermoregulatory mechanisms. For instance, the deer mouse (*Peromyscus maniculatus*) lives in burrows that provide considerable thermal stability despite intolerable external variations in temperature. Burrow temperature varies by a maximum of about 26 K during external variations of some 60 K ; during a diurnal macroclimatic fluctuation in summer of some 16 K, the burrow temperature remains almost constant (fig. 7.1).

7.1.1. *Latitude and Season*

The chief impact of climate on animals results from differences of geographical location or of season. The distribution of both poikilo-thermic and homoiothermic species is profoundly affected by latitude, although many animals remain dormant throughout a large part of the year while conditions are unfavourable in terms of energy balance. Unfortunately, many of the effects of season and latitude cannot easily be ascribed to particular climatic factors, because the responses of organisms are influenced by so complex an array of phenomena, some of them environmental, some hereditary. Thermal factors in the environment commonly interact with the fundamental endogenous rhythms in a way which is extremely difficult for the biologist to unravel.

Structural responses to climate occur in relation to both seasonal and geographic changes, and may be advantageous in relieving the need for physiological responses which are more costly. Alterations in the thickness of fur or plumage would fall into this category, providing insulative protection against cold during winter. The traditional ' laws ' of C. Bergmann and J. A. Allen are also relevant. Although they were formulated in the nineteenth century and have been much criticized in more recent times, they remain useful guides with a sound physical foundation, and are not wholly invalidated just because many exceptions have been described. Bergmann's rule says essentially that, in a given species, races of larger size will occur in cooler parts of the range, and those of smaller size in warmer parts. Allen's rule states that the size of the appendages in a given species decreases in the cooler parts of the range compared to the warmer parts. The rules are only generalizations, but they do make functional sense, as a look at the surface area considerations in Chapter 2 will confirm.

Changes which occur in the thickness of the coat are commonly related to the reproductive cycle, which itself is governed primarily by changes in photoperiod as seen naturally in altering day-length. Short, or shortening, day-length, is a prerequisite for the moult that precedes development of the winter coat in many mammals, while a period of lengthening days is necessary in birds to stimulate gonadal growth and the annual moult. Since changes in light generally precede those in temperature, the light-related alterations in insulation seem to be a convenient preparation for thermal stress.

The insulative changes in birds and mammals that relate to season and latitude are often accompanied by metabolic adaptations. Thus, with the lowering of the critical temperature in winter there is commonly a concurrent reduction in the metabolic response to cooling of the environment. Enhanced cold-resistance may also be achieved by the more expensive method of increasing the capacity to produce body heat, a type of response which is especially important in smaller animals in which insulative protection is limited.

Unfortunately we still have a great deal to learn about the stimuli involved in natural seasonal modifications, and the problem is especially difficult because laboratory experiments tend grossly to over-simplify in that they typically involve the alteration of one environmental variable at a time. In nature there seems always to be an interaction of several factors more or less simultaneously, among them temperature, light and the availability of food.

7.2. THE NATURE OF ADAPTATION

The way in which organisms respond to changes in their environment is an old topic of interest to biologists. The responses vary according to the temporal characteristics of the change as well as according to its magnitude. In a general way, we say that alterations exhibited by living organisms which favour their survival are adaptive. Adaptation seems to be a fundamental characteristic of living material ; the greater the degree of adaptation to change, the greater is the likelihood that the material will survive to reproduce its kind.

The study of adaptation to environmental change is yet another area of biology that has been plagued by arguments over terminology. Fortunately, the only aspect of this that need concern us in the distinction between the words ' acclimatization ' and ' acclimation '. For our purpose, acclimatization is used to describe compensatory changes in an animal acquired in nature, whereas acclimation refers to such changes acquired under laboratory conditions. It is unlikely that the two differ in any fundamental sense, but the distinction is perhaps worth keeping because of the artificial nature of the laboratory environment.

We saw in Chapter 1 how it is convenient to divide animals into those that adapt by conformity and those that adapt by regulation.

The second category is of more interest to us, but it is important to consider the first type in a little more detail, for it is by conformity that the great majority of animals adjust to changes in the thermal environment. As we know, biological processes such as heart or breathing rate and the rate of enzyme reactions, are determined in poikilothermic animals by the temperature to which the creature is accustomed. If the temperature is altered abruptly, a given rate typically shows a shock reaction or over-shoot, before settling down to a new stabilized value which may last unchanged for many hours. When the animal is then returned to its previous thermal conditions the rate also regains its initial level.

If, however, the animal is maintained for several days at the new temperature, the rate of a process may show adaptation to the new conditions. There would then be a secondary, acquired change in the rate which would differ from the stabilized rate achieved on first exposure to the new temperature. Furthermore, if the animal were now

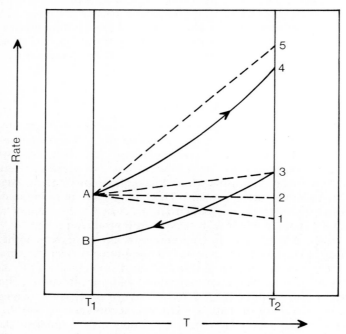

Fig. 7.2. Precht's classification of types of acclimation to temperature. If an animal acclimated to T_1 (A) is transferred to T_2 the rate of a given process rises along the upper continuous line. If partial acclimation to T_2 occurs (point 3) and the animal is then returned to T_1, the rate falls along the lower continuous line to B. (Modified from Precht *et al.*, *Temperatur und Leben*, 1955.)

returned to its original temperature, the rate would not return to the original level, but rather to a level higher or lower than the original. That is, acclimation would have occurred.

In general, there are two schemes available to biologists for describing the types of acclimation observed in poikilotherms to changing thermal environments. That devised by J. Precht compares the rate of a biological process at one acclimation temperature with that at a second (fig. 7.2). For example, if an animal accustomed to one temperature is transferred to a higher temperature, the rate rises to a new, higher level. Over several days, if there were no acclimation, the rate would remain

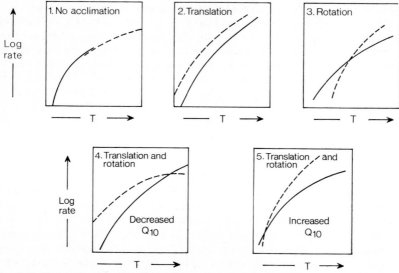

Fig. 7.3. Prosser's classification of types of acclimation to temperature. 1. No change in the rate of a process after adaptation to a new temperature. 2. Shift of curve to left on cold acclimation (translation). 3. Rotation about a central axis, changing the Q_{10}. 4 and 5. A combination of translation and rotation. (Redrawn and modified from Prosser in Dill, *Handbook of Physiology, Adaptation to the Environment*, 1964.)

at this new level (pattern 4 in fig. 7.2). If, on the other hand, acclimation were complete, the rate would be the same at the higher temperature as at the first temperature (pattern 2). More commonly, partial acclimation occurs so that the level falls between the two (pattern 3). In rarer circumstances there may be either over-compensation (pattern 1) or under-compensation (pattern 5).

The second scheme is that of C. L. Prosser, in which the responses of warmth-acclimated and cold-acclimated animals are compared over a wide range of temperatures (fig. 7.3). There are three basic types of response. When there has been no acclimation, the curve for the rate of a given process will simply be continuous. Commonly, the curve is shifted either to the right or to the left without effect on its slope ; such a change is called translation. In the case of cold-acclimation, the shift would generally be to the left, giving a higher rate for a given temperature. In some cases there is a change in the slope of the curve, a phenomenon called rotation. This indicates an altered Q_{10}. Most often of all, acclimation occurs by a combination of both translation and rotation. Again, in the case of cold-acclimation, a fall of Q_{10} accompanied by a shift of the curve to the left will result in the intersection of the two curves at a high temperature ; conversely, a rise in Q_{10} and a shift of the curve to the left will result in intersection at a low temperature.

The value of these schemes is that they provide a systematic basis for the comparison of acclimation in different animals. It is sometimes argued that the type of response exhibited suggests the underlying mechanism of the adaptation ; thus Prosser's translation type of response is said to reflect a change in enzyme activity. Unfortunately, however, the vagueness of this idea tells us little and it must be admitted that we still have a very poor understanding of the effects of temperature at the biochemical level. As we shall see, this applies equally well to animals that adapt by regulation.

7.3. *ADAPTATION TO COLD*

If a homoiotherm is abruptly exposed to a cold environment there follow immediately a number of reflex responses designed to conserve body heat. These reflexes are mediated by way of the skin cold-receptors. There is maximum constriction of peripheral blood vessels, erection of hair or feathers, and frequently a reduction of functional surface area by changes of posture. (The erection of hair is represented in man by what is popularly known as gooseflesh. The erector muscles —see fig. 4.13 B—may be reflexly contracted by the activity of adrenergic sympathetic nerves, more notably in response to tactile stimuli than to cold, and it is doubtful, to say the least, if the phenomenon now has any significance in thermoregulation.)

If the exposure continues, and if the heat-conservation mechanisms are insufficient to prevent a fall in deep body temperature, there is an increase in muscle tone which may ultimately be followed by overt shivering. Heat production may further be raised by the activities of the adrenal and thyroid hormones, and in some animals at least this hormone-controlled (non-shivering) thermogenesis may gradually take over the burden of heat production from the more expensive shivering.

The increased heat production that occurs below the critical environmental temperature reaches what is called the summit metabolism at the lower critical temperature. This is the lowest environmental temperature at which the animal's core temperature can be maintained, but it is not the absolute peak of the heat production curve. The latter, or maximal metabolism, is reached when body temperature has already started to fall at environmental temperatures below the lower critical level (see figs. 1.8 and 3.1). This can be of very short-term value only, however, for the enormously rapid expenditure of energy outstrips the rate at which it can be replaced by feeding in a hostile climate.

An animal in the cold is faced with the problem of maintaining a steep thermal gradient between its body core and the environment, and there are three potential ways in which long-term adaptation to cold may be achieved. These are by a reduction of the body temperature, by an improvement in surface insulation, or by an increase in the metabolic heat production.

Since heat loss is proportional to the body-to-environment gradient, a reduction in central temperature, by reducing this gradient, would reduce the loss of heat. However, there is no evidence from either birds or mammals that exposure to cold lasting several weeks causes any adaptation of body temperature itself. While arctic birds have deep

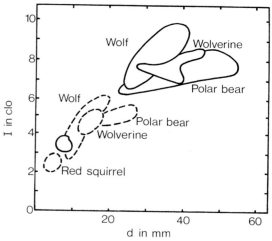

Fig. 7.4. The effect of season on thickness and effective insulation of fur. Continuous lines are mean values in winter; broken lines in summer. (Redrawn and modified by permission of the National Research Council of Canada from Hart, *Can. J. Zool.*, **34**, pp. 53–57, 1956.)

body temperatures on average some 3 K higher than arctic mammals, there is no significant difference between the core temperatures of arctic animals and those of tropical regions. This is an important point, and it indicates that the processes of adaptation must rather be insulative or metabolic.

Measurements of insulation show that the coat of arctic animals generally provides far greater protection than that of animals living in warm regions. Further to this, it is common knowledge that insulation in mammals is highly adaptive to climate ; moulting, followed by the growth of a summer or winter coat, occurs in many species during natural acclimatization or artificial acclimation. We saw in Chapter 2 how the insulation provided by fur increases with thickness, and seasonal changes in insulation within species of arctic mammals range from 12 to 52 per cent, the greatest changes occurring in the larger animals (fig. 7.4) in which the ratio of surface area to mass is smaller. As we should expect, these alterations are reflected in differences of critical temperature.

Insulation plays an important role in cold-adaptation in birds also, and this is of special interest because the feathers serve not only for insulation but also for flight, while in aquatic species they repel the water and minimize the resistance to movement through it. Since most birds avoid severe seasonal cold stress by migration, it may be that these latter functions take precedence over the insulative role, because the requirements for flight and swimming are much the same in all climates and might be interfered with by marked changes in feather thickness

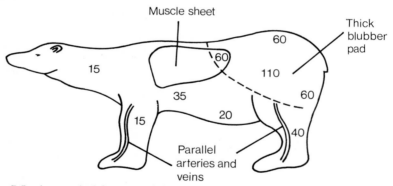

Fig. 7.5. Anatomical features of the polar bear (*Thalarctos maritimus*) adapting it to its semi-aquatic existence. The figures are for blubber thickness in mm. (Based on Oritsland, *Comp. Biochem. Physiol.*, 1970.)

and posture. Birds that over-winter in cold climates, however, undoubtedly show increases in plumage thickness comparable to those in mammals ; the overall weight of the feathers increases and there is commonly a high rate of growth of the down feathers which provide most of the insulation. A large bird such as the glaucous gull (*Larus hyperboreus*) is certainly adapted in this way, having so low a critical temperature that there is almost never the need for a metabolic response, but smaller species seldom appear capable of withstanding very cold conditions by insulation alone, and there are probably none in the Arctic during the winter darkness.

A semi-aquatic mammal such as the polar bear (*Thalarctos maritimus*) depends more on subcutaneous blubber than on fur insulation when it is in the water; although the fur is the main component of insulation in cold still air, it plays an insignificant role in the bear submerged in water. The blubber is up to 110 mm thick over the dorsal abdomen, and an interesting adaptation may be the presence of sheets of striated muscle some 2 mm thick between the layers of fat just under the skin (fig. 7.5). These seem to act as heat exchangers when the bears encounter warm weather or when they generate heat by exercise, for they are provided with a rich supply of blood vessels mostly in the form of arteries and veins in parallel pairs. Heat exchange also occurs in more conventional fashion in the limbs. The adaptations of polar bears to the aquatic environment may have resulted in some loss of effective thermoregulatory ability while on land. Over-heating is always a danger in summer (and often in captivity), while in winter during a strong wind the bears rely heavily on postural adjustments and yet are still unable to avoid a much greater fall in skin temperature than that seen in other large mammals resident in a cold climate.

Large animals, then, depend principally on increased insulation in the cold, but smaller species are limited in their capacity to achieve this and commonly rely more on metabolic adjustments. A warmth-acclimated rat exposed to 5°C exhibits a rapid acceleration of metabolism during the first few days, followed by a slower increase. After about 30 days there is a gradual decline, but the rate of heat production remains substantially above the pre-exposure level, apparently indefinitely. The increased capacity for heat production is generally shown, not only at the low temperature of acclimation, but also at any temperature below the critical level. The degree of this increase is related to the temperature of acclimation. Thus rats acclimated to 0–2°C show a higher heat production at all levels of environmental temperature below the critical than do rats acclimated to 16–20°C. The implication of this sort of experiment is, of course, that animals adapted to lower temperatures are more cold-resistant than animals adapted to higher temperatures; their critical temperatures are lower and they are able to maintain a warmer body surface and can therefore move about more freely in the cold.

In a very small mammal such as the masked shrew (*Sorex cinereus*) with a mass of only about 3 g, a constant body temperature of about 39°C is maintained over an environmental temperature range from 5 to 32°C. Throughout this considerable range, insulation seems to be varied by means of vasomotor and postural changes, and the surprisingly low critical temperature is the result of a metabolism that is three times as high as would be expected, even for a mammal of this minute size.

Oxygen consumption is about 9 cm^3 g^{-1} hr^{-1}, a level that is maintained only by eating every 15 minutes, so that a basal rate is never achieved.

The mechanism responsible for the increased heat production varies according to species. Shivering is the only means so far found in adult birds, while in many mammals non-shivering thermogenesis gradually takes over from shivering as cold-acclimation develops. The exact role of brown fat in adult mammals is still not clear, although it represents only a tiny fraction of body weight and may therefore exert its influence indirectly by warming temperature receptors in the cervical spinal cord and in some way regulating the shivering response. Alternatively, the brown fat may secrete some hormone-like substance which elevates thermogenesis in other tissues. Thyroid hormones are certainly involved in the increased metabolism observed in some animals, while hormone-controlled changes in carbohydrate metabolism may be responsible for providing the extra glucose needed for shivering.

There have been almost no studies on man genuinely exposed to prolonged cold, and we therefore have virtually no information on how he adjusts, even though it is obvious that he does. Men on polar expeditions generally spend only a small proportion of their time outside, and in any case modern clothing is so efficient that the microclimate to which they are exposed is even then more tropical than arctic. There is no direct evidence of metabolic adaptation, although it does appear that the need for clothing may diminish after prolonged residence in a cold climate. Thus in the wet, windy, sub-antarctic climate of Macquarie Island, significantly less insulation was selected for the upper body after a year's residence compared with the early days, and this was certainly confirmed by the subjective impression of enhanced cold-hardiness. In these conditions, it was not possible to show any adaptations of the extremities to cold during the year but there is good evidence of this in colder, drier climates, and also in fishermen accustomed to working for long periods with bare hands in cold water. The adaptation is presumably in the form of changes in peripheral blood flow, specifically the ' hunting ' reaction of cold vasodilatation.

7.3.1. Primitive Man

Some interesting observations have been performed on various groups of primitive men who are naturally exposed to a degree of cold stress. A comparison of the results with those obtained on similarly exposed Europeans provides some basis for evolutionary speculation.

If we look briefly at the findings on two of the best studied groups which happen to exhibit quite different responses, this will be sufficient for our purpose. The Australian aborigines have been examined in central Australia, where the summer diurnal temperature range is about 22–37°C and the winter range about 4–21°C. The night-time temperature imposes a considerable stress on the naked human body and the aborigines counter this to some extent by building rough shelters against the wind and by lying between small fires. The fires, however, are attended only when the sleeper is so cold that he has been aroused. This degree of cold exposure is extremely uncomfortable for the unclothed European, who is accustomed to sleeping with a high and uniform skin temperature.

A second group is represented by the Alacaluf Indians of Tierra del Fuego, the people who were marvelled at by Charles Darwin (1809–82) in his voyage in HMS *Beagle*. Their climate is wet and cold. Although the air temperature may fall below freezing, it is generally around 10°C by day and somewhat cooler at night ; however, loss of heat from the

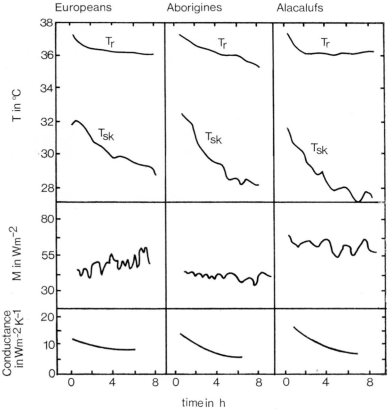

Fig. 7.6. Responses of three groups of men to a night of moderate cold exposure. The values are averages for several individuals of each group. (Based on data from Hammel *et al.*, *J. appl. Physiol.*, 1959 and Wright Air Development Division Tech. Rep. 60–633, 1960.)

body is rapid because of the high winds and frequent rain and sleet. The Indians were examined by methods exactly the same as those employed with the aborigines, although the former slept in thin sleeping bags and without the heat of fires.

Apart from details, there were three distinct patterns of response to the moderate cold-exposures experienced by the indigenous populations and the European investigators during these studies (fig. 7.6). The Europeans themselves started the night-long exposure with a metabolic rate at or about the basal level. As their body temperatures fell during the night, so the metabolic heat production rose sharply by up to 50 per cent by the early morning hours. The Australian aborigines also began the night with metabolic rates near to the basal level. As their body temperatures fell, however, there was an overall decline in metabolic rate, even though the degree of cooling, as shown by both deep body and skin temperatures, was rather greater than that experienced by the Europeans. Finally, a third pattern of response was shown by the Alacaluf Indians. They began the night's sleep with substantially elevated metabolic rates which declined gradually as the night progressed, falling to about the same level of heat production by morning as the Europeans were capable of achieving by that time as a result of their gradual acceleration of metabolism.

The two groups of primitive men thus showed clear signs of acclimatization to the cold nocturnal exposures. The form adopted by the aborigines is insulative and hypothermic. There is a significant loss of heat content from the body core but no metabolic compensation. Additionally, the conductance of the body shell is about 30 per cent less than in Europeans under the same conditions (despite less subcutaneous fat in the aborigines), indicating an improved vasomotor response. Acclimatization in the Alacaluf Indians is clearly metabolic, without an improved insulation or hypothermia. In both groups, another important adaptation was the ability to sleep soundly despite much lower peripheral temperatures than the Europeans could tolerate comfortably.

The insulative–hypothermic form of acclimatization would seem to be appropriate for regions of the earth where the degree of cold stress is no more than moderate, but where food and water are frequently scarce. The night temperatures of the Australian desert are seldom low enough to threaten the extremities with freezing, and the normal body temperature is rapidly and economically restored at dawn by the heat of the sun. The total energy requirements for the eight-hour night, measured on a relative basis, were 20 per cent less for the aborigines than for the Europeans, which might represent a saving of perhaps 5 per cent in total daily energy requirements. In addition, the insulative acclimatization appears more suitable in a climate which is often intensely hot in the day, and where any form of metabolic compensation like that of the Alacaluf Indians might impose a further strain in a situation where water is in short supply.

The opposite might be said to apply to the Indians. Where air temperatures are commonly close to freezing it would be hazardous to allow the skin temperature at the extremities to drop too low. Furthermore, food and water are more readily available to the Alacalufs than to the aborigines, so that the expense of metabolic acclimatization can be met more easily. Since the metabolic response to moderate cold exposure can apparently be maintained for long periods, it might also be an advantage in case of unexpected exposure to severe cold.

The responses of primitive man are of interest in relation to theories of the origin and development of the human species. The reactions to cold exposure of the Australian aborigines may well have been that adopted by the early hominids, for there is nowhere on earth where nocturnal temperatures do not on occasion fall substantially below the critical temperature, which for modern Europeans is about 28°C. If the early men were unclothed and had not discovered fire, the most probable way of countering the moderate stress of night temperature would have been the insulative, hypothermic response. If they were already essentially hairless it would certainly have been the most economical way of passing the low temperatures of the night.

Exploration of somewhat cooler regions became possible with the discovery of fire, but survival in the temperate zone could not have occurred until the use of animal fur provided the necessary insulation against the winter temperatures. The use of clothing is of special interest because it provides a microclimate of an almost tropical variety such that direct exposure to cold is completely avoided. It also removes the need for the dual acclimatization to both heat and cold which we have seen in the aborigines, for the microclimate is one of perpetual moderate warmth. With the development of shelters and housing the need to tolerate cold at any season was further reduced, and it is probable that these changes were accompanied by the loss of the ability to sleep during mild cold exposure. Thus the modern European, accustomed to a protected environment, sleeps comfortably only with a microclimate sufficiently warm to relax the vasoconstrictor tone of the peripheral arterioles and create a skin temperature all over the body of about 33°C.

7.4. ADAPTATION TO HEAT

When an animal is placed in a hot environment the warmth receptors in the skin are stimulated to initiate the various reflex responses which favour the dissipation of heat. Peripheral vasodilatation occurs and with it an enhanced flow of blood to the skin causing an increase in the conductance of the surface tissues. In some species the skin receptors also elicit the panting or sweating responses that dissipate heat by evaporation of water, while in others a rise in the temperature of the hypothalamus is necessary before these occur.

Prolonged exposure to heat results in a number of changes which are the consequence of the primary responses to acute exposure. Vaso-dilatation is accompanied by a redistribution of blood, largely by means of a reduction in flow to the kidneys and visceral circulation. Over a period of several days there is commonly an increase in blood volume. This is necessary to maintain circulatory efficiency, notably the blood pressure, in the face of massive peripheral vasodilatation. With in-creasing acclimation, the sweating and panting responses are often seen to occur at lower threshold temperatures (thus minimizing heat stress) and, in the case of sweating, the output of moisture may increase by up to 25 per cent. Water and electrolyte turnover is profoundly affected under these conditions, and there is a marked reduction in urine output and a retention of salt by the kidneys and sweat glands. The initial loss of salt that occurs in sweating animals during acute exposure to heat is thus brought under control, although the re-establishment of normal salt and water balance obviously depends on the intake in the diet.

The hot desert represents one of the most stressful environments for animal life, because the intense heat of the day (which may be followed by considerable cold stress at night) is typically combined with a limited supply of water. Since heat loss by the direct channels is often impossible in the day, evaporation may be the only physiological means available and this, unfortunately, requires a plentiful water supply. Despite this situation, many animals have adapted successfully to life in the deserts, and their mechanisms of survival depend very largely upon whether they are large or small. We can hardly do better than illustrate the problems by reference to Schmidt-Nielsen's work on the camel and the kangaroo rat.

Contrary to popular belief, the camel does not owe its success in the desert climate to the storage of water. The hump does not contain water but is made largely of fat. While the oxidation of fat does yield water, this process itself requires oxygen, and the increased ventilation of the lungs that is necessary to provide it accelerates the rate of evaporative loss of water so that overall the balance is negative. Camels seek out shade when it is available, but if it is not they merely sit down in the cool of the morning, tuck the legs under the body, and remain still all day while exposing as little body surface to the sun as possible. The relatively thick covering of hair on the upper surface acts as an efficient protection against solar radiation ; thus a shorn camel depends far more than does an unshorn one on the evaporation of water.

If the camel is able to drink freely its body temperature remains about as stable as that of other large homoiotherms. However, when it is deprived of water the diurnal fluctuations of deep body temperature may exceed 6·0 K (fig. 7.7). That there are apparently limits to these oscillations has been considered evidence in favour of Bligh's ' broad-band ' thermoregulatory control (Chapter 6). This instability of body temperature represents an important adaptation to water economy, and it is now known to be used by other large animals (e.g. the eland, *Taurotragus oryx*) that inhabit the hot, arid regions of East Africa. There are two advantages of having a labile body temperature. First, water that would otherwise have to be expended to keep the body temperature down is saved ; the excess heat accumulated during the day is lost to the cool air at night without the use of water. Second, the raised body temperature creates a more favourable body-to-environment thermal gradient so that more heat is lost by radiation and convection in moderate conditions, while at very high temperatures less is gained by

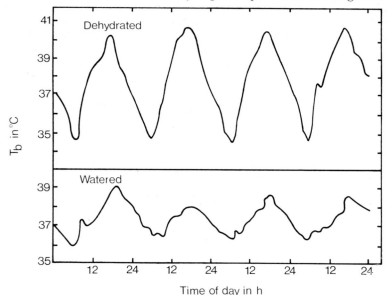

Fig. 7.7. The effect of dehydration on the diurnal fluctuations in deep body temperature in the camel. (Redrawn from Schmidt-Nielsen *et al.*, *Am. J. Physiol.*, 1957.)

the body from the environment. This therefore reduces the quantity of water that may have to be expended to prevent a further elevation of body temperature.

Only a large animal can utilize water-economy measures of this sort. The camel has a ratio of mass to surface area that is roughly twenty times as favourable as that of the kangaroo rat, which means that the same rate of heat gain per unit surface area would cause the body temperature of the kangaroo rat to rise twenty times as fast as the rate of the camel. The small animal would very quickly die in hyperthermia, and this is why the kangaroo rat survives the desert only by avoiding the worst of the desert climate. It is nocturnal in habit, and stays in its burrow throughout the heat of the day, thus avoiding the use of water for temperature regulation. This is a fine example of behavioural adaptation going hand in hand with physiological adaptation, for the kangaroo rat, under normal conditions, never drinks. It lives chiefly on dry seeds and other dry plant material, and selects these even when green and succulent plants are available. Even the air-dried food contains a small amount of water and this, coupled with the water formed during the oxidation of food (metabolic water) is sufficient to provide for the animal's scanty needs, so efficiently has it minimized the rate of water loss (fig. 7.8).

All animals are bound to lose a certain amount of water through evaporation, as well as in the formation of urine and faeces. The camel sweats in the heat, though no more than is absolutely necessary. Its sweat evaporates from the surface of the skin, which is the most

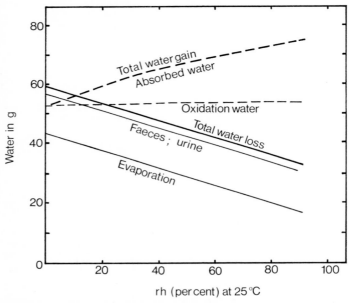

Fig. 7.8. The dependence of water balance in the kangaroo rat on the relative humidity (rh) of the atmosphere. The water losses in evaporation, urine and faeces are superimposed to give the total water loss (heavy continuous line). Water gains from oxidation and directly from food are treated likewise (heavy broken line). Where the two heavy lines intersect the rat is just in water balance. Water gains increase to the right while water losses fall; to the left of the intersection, however, the rat would be in negative water balance. (Redrawn and modified from Schmidt-Nielsen and Schmidt-Nielsen, *J. cell. comp. Physiol.*, 1951.)

effective point so far as heat loss from the body is concerned ; the dry fur serves as a barrier between the hot air and the cool skin. The kangaroo rat has sweat glands only on the foot pads, and appears to lose virtually no water through the skin. By contrast, the white rat, which also lacks general sweat glands, loses as much moisture by insensible perspiration through the skin as it does through the respiratory tract in breathing. The kangaroo rat also evaporates relatively little water in its expired air, an economy which is achieved by lowering the temperature of the air by contact with the cool nasal tubes so that a good deal of its water is deposited on the mucosa (see Section 4.2.1).

Both the camel and kangaroo rat excrete very dry faeces, and in the case of the latter the utilization of food material is unusually high so that the quantity of faeces per unit food intake is low. Faecal water loss in this species is only about one-fifth that of a white rat of the same size. Both desert species also have very powerful kidneys which can produce a highly-concentrated urine ; much of the water is reabsorbed so that little is lost in urine formation. The camel can secrete urine whose salt content is higher than that of sea water, while the kangaroo rat produces a urine whose salt is twice as high. When fed solely on soybeans, which have a very high protein content and therefore yield large quantities of urea which have to be excreted, kangaroo rats have to resort to drinking. When provided only with sea water under these conditions, they thrive. This performance is in marked contrast to that of man, whose most concentrated urine has only about two-thirds the salt content of sea water. Thus if a marooned mariner resorts to drinking sea water he would lose one and a half times as much water in excreting the unwanted salts as he drank in attempting to quench his thirst, thus suffering a further water deficit. The kangaroo rat, on the other hand, would excrete the salts using only half the water consumed.

We have already encountered in Chapter 4 the extraordinary tolerance of dehydration possessed by the camel. Whereas most animals suffer an explosive rise in body temperature if 15 per cent of the body weight is lost as water, the camel can tolerate up to twice this level without ill effects. By an unknown mechanism, the plasma volume is maintained constant during dehydration, so that added strain on the circulation is avoided. The capacity for replacing lost water is also enormous, such that all can be replaced at a single sitting.

In contrast to the situation in mammals where tolerance of hyper-thermia appears to be an adaptive response only among large species, it seems that birds of all sizes use this device in the desert environment. Since this is in addition to the already high level of body temperature characteristic of birds, hyperthermia can have considerable significance as a means of reducing the need for the evaporation of water. Temperatures from 43–44°C are commonly tolerated for several hours, by desert and non-desert species alike when exposed to heat, although it is not surprising that birds deprived of water develop a greater hyperthermia than drinking birds. The ostrich, which shares with the camel many of the advantages of large size, can maintain its body temperature at the normal level for several hours in air temperatures as high as 51°C by evaporative cooling, but when deprived of water it reduces its rate of evaporation and allows the body temperature to rise. A similar response has been described also for the budgerigar, and it seems likely that an altered pattern of temperature regulation, with reduced evaporation, may be a common response among both birds and mammals to the combined stresses of intense heat and water lack.

Another form of adaptation to hot climates is the reduction of metabolism. This is now known to be widespread among a variety of species. In man, residents of the tropics have a slightly lower basal metabolic rate than those of temperate areas, while mice and voles native to hot climates have metabolic rates lower than would be predicted on the basis of body weight. Fowls acclimated to hot conditions have a lower rate of heat production than those accustomed to cool temperatures, while house sparrows introduced into the hot, humid regions of Texas have lower metabolic rates and higher evaporative efficiencies than sparrows introduced to cooler regions of the United States.

The reduced heat production is almost certainly under hormonal control. There is good evidence of a reduction in thyroid activity in the heat, while the fall in body weight which is a common response to hot climates may be related to a reduction in the relative mass of such heat-producing organs as the liver, kidney, heart and pads of brown fat. There is also some suggestion that the oxidative enzyme activity in liver mitochondria may be reduced by heat.

Other endocrine effects important in adaptation to heat include the increased secretion of the antidiuretic hormone (ADH) from the pituitary, which is responsible for the reduction in urine volume described in many animals, and the increased output of aldosterone from the cortex of the adrenal glands, which minimizes the loss of salt from the kidney and sweat glands. This last response is best understood in man ; the role of aldosterone in other homoiotherms has not yet been resolved, although salt losses tend, in any case, to be far smaller. The mechanism of action of aldosterone is still not known for certain, although it may increase the capacity for sodium reabsorption in the duct of the sweat glands in a manner which is proportional to the increase in sweat production.

7.4.1. *Human Adaptation*

Just as we saw with cold exposure, the physiology of man in the heat has special interest in relation to the recent evolution of our species. The differentiation of man's ancestors from the primate stock probably involved a gradual change in habitat from the forest to the open grasslands or savanna of the equatorial zone in the Pliocene period. This change must have been accompanied by significant alterations in physiological adaptation to climatic heat. In the tropical forest the daytime temperatures typically range from 28–32°C, there is very little air movement, little direct solar radiation, but very high humidity reaching almost to saturation. Our ancestors, when inactive, would have experienced little heat stress since metabolic heat could be readily lost by radiation. When active, however, stress could easily be encountered because evaporative heat loss is inefficient.

The forest contrasts rather sharply with the savanna, where the chief problem is that of solar radiation, causing high direct and reflected radiant heat loads. In the daytime, convective and radiant heat transfer could easily be from environment to body and the main burden of heat loss would fall on the sweating mechanism.

Because all other primates possess a thick, hairy coat, it is generally assumed that man's ancestors were once similarly clad and that the loss of hair was an adaptive advantage in hot conditions. Thus it is argued that the hair was lost as the need for efficient sweating increased under the high solar irradiation of the savanna environment. However, while the possession of a hair coat must reduce the rate of evaporation of sweat, there are indications from other mammals that this may be more than offset by the effect of the coat in reducing the heat load from the sun. It might equally well be, therefore, that man's nakedness was a disadvantage when he emerged into the direct sun and that his highly efficient sweating mechanism was developed in response to this situation. If this be so, the loss of bodily hair must have occurred for reasons other than temperature regulation in the sun, perhaps as a result of a neotenous development in his earlier evolution. Certainly it might be argued that nakedness would be more an advantage in the thermally stable forest than on the open plain.

The curious thing about man's dependence on the sweating response during heat exposure is that it is not accompanied by any of the other adaptations seen in other sweating mammals. Profuse sweating quickly leads to dehydration, yet man is very intolerant of this condition, and cannot rehydrate rapidly or accurately even when drinking water is available. In contrast to many other animals, man is dependent upon frequent and relatively small drinks of water in the heat, and we can only guess at the ways in which this must have influenced specific behaviour. We still have too little knowledge of how other primates react to natural heat stress, but it is unlikely that any depends upon sweating to the same extent as does man. Behavioural avoidance both of heat stress and of water deprivation are more probable. It seems that man's unique predicament was solved by his unique success at technological adaptation, perhaps first by the invention of water carriers and later by providing for himself a protected cryptoclimate.

BIBLIOGRAPHY

BENZINGER, T. H. (1961). The human thermostat. *Scient. Am.*, **204** (Jan.), 134–147.

BENZINGER, T. H. (1969). Heat regulation : homoiostasis of central temperature in man. *Physiol. Rev.*, **49**, 671–759.

BLIGH, J. (1966). The thermosensitivity of the hypothalamus and thermoregulation in mammals. *Biol. Rev.*, **41**, 317–367.

BURTON, A. C. and EDHOLM, O. G. (1955). *Man in a Cold Environment.* Arnold, London.

CHAFFEE, R. R. J. and ROBERTS, J. C. (1971). Temperature acclimation in birds and mammals. *Ann. Rev. Physiol.*, **33**, 155–202.

COLLINS, K. J. and WEINER, J. S. (1968). Endocrinological aspects of exposure to high environmental temperature. *Physiol. Rev.*, **48**, 785–839.

DAWKINS, M. J. R. and HULL, D. (1965). The production of heat by fat. *Scient. Am.*, **213** (Aug.), 62–67.

DILL, D. B. (editor) (1964). Handbook of physiology, Sec. 4, Adaptation to environment. *Am. Physiol. Soc.*, Washington.

HAMMEL, H. T. (1968). Regulation of internal body temperature. *Ann. Rev. Physiol.*, **30**, 641–710.

HANNON, J. P. and VIERECK, E. (editors) (1962). *Comparative Physiology of Temperature Regulation.* Arctic Aeromed. Lab., Fort Wainwright, Alaska.

HARDY, J. D. (1961). Physiology of temperature regulation. *Physiol. Rev.*, **41**, 521–606.

HEMMINGWAY, A. (1963). Shivering. *Physiol. Rev.*, **43**, 397–422.

IRVING, L. (1966). Adaptations to cold. *Scient. Am.*, **214** (Jan.), 94–101.

KAYSER, C. (1961). *The Physiology of Natural Hibernation.* Pergamon, Oxford.

KERSLAKE, D. McK. (1972). *The Stress of Hot Environments.* University Press, Cambridge.

LEWIS, H. E. (1971). How man survives the cold. *Science J.* (Jan.), 29–32.

MARTIN, C. J. (1903). Thermal adjustment and respiratory exchange in monotremes and marsupials. *Phil. Trans. R. Soc.* B, **195**, 1–37.

MOUNT, L. E. (1968). *The Climatic Physiology of the Pig.* Arnold, London.

RICHARDS, S. A. (1970). The biology and comparative physiology of thermal panting. *Biol. Rev.*, **45**, 223–264.

SALT, G. W. (1964). Respiratory evaporation in birds. *Biol. Rev.*, **39**, 113–136.

SCHMIDT-NIELSEN, K. (1959). The physiology of the camel. *Scient. Am.*, **201** (Dec.), 140–151.

SCHMIDT-NIELSEN, K. (1964). *Desert Animals: Physiological Problems of Heat and Water.* Clarendon Press, Oxford.

SMITH, R. E. and HORWITZ, B. A. (1969). Brown fat and thermogenesis. *Physiol. Rev.*, **49**, 330–426.

TAYLOR, C. R. (1969). The eland and the oryx. *Scient. Am.*, **220** (Jan.), 88–95.

WEINER, J. S. and HELLMAN, K. (1960). The sweat glands. *Biol. Rev.*, **35**, 141–186.

WHITTOW, G. C. (editor) (1970–71). *Comparative Physiology of Thermoregulation.* Vol. I, *Invertebrates and Non-mammalian Vertebrates.* Vol. II, *Mammals.* Academic Press, London.

GLOSSARY

Action potential. Electrical potential difference associated with impulse conduction in nerve or muscle ; localized changes of potential between the inside and outside of the fibre.

Amine. A compound in which one hydrogen atom of ammonia (NH_3) is replaced by a hydrocarbon group (e.g. $C_2H_5NH_2$, ethylamine).

Amino acid. Organic acid containing a carboxyl group (–COOH) and an amino group ($-NH_2$). The building blocks of proteins.

Carboniferous. Geological period lasting approximately from 260 to 200 million years ago.

Electrode. Metallic contact to an electric circuit. In physiology, generally an insulated wire for detecting potential changes associated with nerve or muscle activity.

Electrolyte. For our purposes, a substance (acid, base or salt) which, when dissolved in water, makes a solution through which an electric current flows by migration of ions. In the body, sodium chloride is the main electrolyte in the blood and tissue spaces ; potassium salts are the main ones in the cells.

Hypothalamus. The floor and sides of the posterior part of the fore-brain. Has close functional connexions with the pituitary gland and exerts ' higher ' control over many physiological processes by its influence on the autonomic nervous system.

Jurassic. Geological period lasting approximately from 160 to 140 million years ago.

Neuroglia. Connective tissue of the nervous system, probably with many functions as yet largely unknown.

Phosphorylase. Enzyme important in glycogen metabolism.

Phosphorylation, oxidative. The enzymic process whereby energy, released from the oxidation-reduction reactions of the electron transfer chain, is conserved by the synthesis of adenosine triphosphate.

Pliocene. Geological period lasting approximately from 15 to 1 million years ago.

Proportionality, constant of. When two variables are so related that their ratio remains constant they are said to be directly proportional, e.g. where $xy^{-1} = k$, where x and y vary proportionately and k is a constant of proportionality.

Spectrometer, mass. Instrument for separating positively charged particles according to their masses by electromagnetic means.

Steroid. Organic compound containing carbon, hydrogen and oxygen and having a characteristic structure of carbon rings, e.g. vitamin D, some fatty acids, sex hormones.

199

Thyroidism. Disturbances in the body related to thyroid function. Hyperthyroidism is the condition due to abnormal increase in thyroid function, with an enlarged gland, e.g. exophthalmic goitre. Hypothyroidism is the condition due to deficient thyroid function, with degeneration of the gland, e.g. myxoedema and cretinism.

Transduction. Conversion of energy from one form to another.

Triassic. Geological period lasting approximately from 180 to 160 million years ago.

Vasomotor. Referring to the regulation of the diameter of blood vessels. The vasomotor centre in the medulla elicits constriction or dilatation of peripheral vessels by way of the autonomic nervous system.

a classified list of the animals featured in the text and illustrations

This is not a complete classification of the animal kingdom, and is intended only to place the species mentioned in their taxonomic context. A more modern name is sometimes given as well as that used by the author quoted in the text. North American vernacular names are given in parentheses where they differ from English ones.

Phylum **ARTHROPODA**
Class **INSECTA**
  Subclass PTERYGOTA
    Order **Dictyoptera** (cockroaches and mantids)
      Blatta orientalis, common cockroach
      Periplaneta americana, American cockroach
    Order **Phthiraptera** (lice)
      Pediculus humanus, human louse
    Order **Hemiptera** (bugs and greenflies)
      Diceroprocta apache, desert cicada
    Order **Lepidoptera** (butterflies and moths)
      Boloria chariclea, arctic chequered butterfly
      Celerio lineata, striated sphinx (hawk) moth
      Manduca sexta, tobacco hornworm (sphinx moth)
    Order **Hymenoptera** (ants, bees and wasps)
      Apis mellifera, honey bee

Class **CRUSTACEA**
  Subclass MALACOSTRACA
    Order **Decapoda** (crabs, lobsters, etc.)
      Uca pugnax, fiddler crab

Phylum **VERTEBRATA**
Class **ACTINOPTERYGII**
  Superorder **Chondrostei**
    Order **Acipenseroidei** (sturgeons)
      Acipenser sturio, common sturgeon
  Superorder **Teleostei**
    Order **Isospondyli** (salmon, trout, herring, etc.)
      Salvelinus fontinalis, American brook trout
    Order **Perciformes** (perch, mackerel, etc.)
      Katsuwonus pelamis, skipjack tunny (tuna)
      Thunnus albacares, yellowfin tunny
      T. thynnus, bluefin tunny

Order **Scleroparei** (mail-cheeked fishes)
  Myoxocephalus scorpoides, arctic sculpin
  M. scorpius, arctic sculpin

Class **AMPHIBIA**
 Order **Salientia = Anura** (frogs and toads)
  Suborder DIPLASIOCOELA
   Rana catesbeina, North American bullfrog
   R. pipiens, leopard frog
  Suborder PROCOELA
   Hyla caerulea, green tree frog
   H. rubella, Australian tree frog

Class **REPTILIA**
 Order **Chelonia** (tortoises and turtles)
  Pseudemys elegans, American freshwater turtle
  Terrapene ornata, box turtle
 Order **Squamata** (lizards and snakes)
  Suborder SAURIA
   Amblyrhynchus cristatus, Galapagos marine iguana
   Cyclodus dorsalis, Australian blue-tongued lizard
   Dipsosaurus dorsalis, desert iguana
   Liolaemus multiformis, Peruvian mountain lizard
   Phrynosoma coronatum, horned lizard
   Sauromalus obesus, chuckwalla
   S. varius, chuckwalla
   Tiliqua scincoides, American blue-tongued lizard
  Suborder SERPENTES
   Natrix taxispilota, brown water snake
   Pituophis catenifer, desert gopher snake
   Python molurus, Indian python
 Order **Crocodilia** (crocodiles, etc.)
  Caiman sclerops, South American caiman
  Crocodilus niloticus, Nile crocodile

Class **AVES**
 Subclass ARCHAEONITHES
  Archaeopteryx lithographica
 Subclass NEORNITHES
 Superorder **Impennes**
 Order **Sphenisciformes** (penguins)
  Pygoscelis papua, gentoo penguin
 Order **Anseriformes** (ducks, geese and swans)
  Anser domesticus, domestic goose
 Order **Apodiformes** (swifts and humming birds)
  Apus apus, common swift
  Selasphorus sasin, Allen humming bird
 Order **Caprimulgiformes** (nightjars, etc.)
  Nyctidromus albicollis, Panama night hawk
  Phalaenoptilus nuttallii, poorwill

Order **Charadriiformes** (plovers, gulls, etc.)
Larus argentatus, herring gull
L. hyperboreus, glaucous gull

Order **Ciconiiformes** (herons, storks, etc.)
Bubulcus ibis, cattle egret

Order **Columbiformes** (pigeons)
Columba livia, pigeon or rock dove
Streptopelia risoria, Barbary dove

Order **Cuculiformes** (cuckoos, etc.)
Geococcyx californianus, roadrunner

Order **Galliformes** (grouse, quail, turkeys, etc.)
Gallus gallus, domestic fowl
Leipoa ocellata, mallee fowl

Order **Passeriformes** (perching birds)
Campylorhynchus brunneicapillus, cactus wren
Certhia brachydactyla, European short-toed tree creeper
Molothrus ater, brown-headed cowbird
Passer domesticus, house sparrow (English Sparrow)
Perisoreus canadensis, Canada jay
Plectrophenax nivalis, snow bunting
Pyrrhuloxia (Richmondena) cardinalis, cardinal
Troglodytes troglodytes, common (winter) wren
Zonotrichia leucophrys, white-crowned sparrow

Superorder **Neognathae**
Order **Procellariiformes** (petrels and albatrosses)
Diomedea nigripes, black-footed albatross

Order **Psittaciformes** (parrots)
Melopsittacus undulatus, budgerigar

Order **Struthioniformes** (ostriches)
Struthio camelus (ostrich)

Class **MAMMALIA**
Subclass PROTOTHERIA
Order **Monotremata** (monotremes)
Ornithorhynchus paradoxus, duck-billed platypus
Tachyglossus hystrix, echidna or spiny anteater

Subclass METATHERIA
Order **Marsupialia** (marsupials)
Bettongia cuniculus, Tasmanian rat kangaroo
Dasyurus (Dasyops) maculatus, marsupial cat
Trichosurus vulpecula, brush-tailed opossum

Subclass EUTHERIA
Order **Insectivora** (hedgehogs, shrews and moles)
Sorex cinereus, masked shrew

S. tundrensis, arctic shrew

Order **Chiroptera** (bats)
Myotis lucifugus, little brown bat

Order **Primates** (primates)
Homo sapiens, man
Leontocebus geoffroyi, marmoset
Macaca mulatta, Indian macaque or common rhesus monkey
Pan satyrus, chimpanzee
Saimiri sciurea, squirrel monkey

Order **Edentata** (anteaters, sloths and armadillos)
Choloepus hoffmanni, two-toed sloth

Order **Lagomorpha** (rabbits, etc.)
Lepus americanus, American hare,
Oryctolagus cuniculus, rabbit

Order **Rodentia** (rodents)

Suborder SCIUROMORPHA
Castor canadensis, beaver
Citellus beecheyi, California ground squirrel
C. citellus, European ground squirrel
C. lateralis, golden-mantled ground squirrel
C. parryii, arctic ground squirrel
Dipodomys merriami, kangaroo rat
Marmota spp., marmots
Tamiasciurus hudsonicus, American red squirrel

Suborder MYOMORPHA
Dicrostonyx groenlandicus (= *D. torquatus*), collared lemming
Eliomys quercinus, European garden dormouse
Mesocricetus auratus, golden hamster
Mus musculus, house mouse
Peromyscus maniculatus, deer mouse
Rattus norvegicus, white rat

Suborder HYSTRICOMORPHA
Cavia porcellus, guinea pig

Order **Carnivora** (carnivores)
Alopex lagopus, fox
Canis familiaris, dog
C. lupus, wolf
Felis domesticus, cat
Gulo gulo, wolverine or glutton
Martes americana, American marten
Mustela rixosa, least weasel
Thalarctos maritimus, polar bear
Ursus arctos (= *U. horribilis*), grizzly bear
Vulpes fulva, American red fox

Order **Pinnipedia** (seals and sea lions)
Phoca hispida, hair seal

Order **Proboscidea** (elephants)
Elephas maximus (Asian elephant)

Order **Perissodactyla** (odd-toed ungulates)
Equus asinus, donkey
E. caballus, horse

Order **Artiodactyla** (even-toed ungulates)
Suborder SUIFORMES
Sus scrofa, pig

Suborder TYLOPODA
Camelus dromedarius, one-humped camel

Suborder RUMINANTIA
Bos taurus, ox
Capra hircus, goat
Ovis aries, sheep
O. dalli, dall sheep
Rangifer tarandus, caribou and domestic reindeer

INDEX

acclimation (see also adaptation) 181
acclimatization (see also adaptation) 6, 181
acetylcholine 103, 175
acid-base equilibrium 93–95
ACTH (see adrenocorticotrophic hormone)
adaptation 5, 181–197
  to cold 184–191
  to heat 191–197
action potential 66–67
activity, voluntary 70–71, 142
adenosine diphosphate 55, 69
adenosine triphosphate 54–55
ADH (see anti-diuretic hormone)
adipose tissue (see also fat), 63–65
ADP (see adenosine diphosphate)
adrenal gland 130
adenaline 65, 80, 174–175
adrenergic nerves 103–104, 122
adrenocorticotrophic hormone 62
aestivation 18, 134–135
air movement 32
air sacs 94–95
Alacaluf Indians 189–191
albatross 136
aldosterone 196
algae 1
Allen's rule 180
altricial development 143–147
amphibians 96, 120–122
ampullae of Lorenzini 119
anabolic processes 52
anaesthesia 152
Andes 123
Antarctic 1
anti-diuretic hormone 196
anti-dromic conduction 82–83
anti-homoiostasis 171
apocrine gland 96–102
aquatic animals 81
Archaeopteryx 9
Arctic 185
arousal (hibernation) 132–133
arteriovenous anastomosis 77
arthropods 96
astronaut 162
ATP (see adenosine triphosphate)

atrichial gland 97–102
Australia 137
Australian aborigines 34, 188–191
autonomic nervous system 81–85, 103, 131, 139
axon reflex 82–83

bacteria 1
Bahamas 117
Barbary dove 136
Barcroft, Joseph 5
basal metabolic rate 40–42, 139
basking 122–113, 122–124
bats 130
bears 18, 130, 134
bees 115
behaviour 10, 110–142, 166–168, 171–172, 197
Benedict, F. G 59
Benzinger, T. H. 162–173
Bergmann, L. 151
Bergmann's rule 180
Bernard, Claude 7, 83
bicycle ergometer 70
biological activities 2–3
birds (see also individual species),
  behavioural responses 135–138
  insulation 186
  origins of homoiothermy 9–10, 143–144
  torpor 130, 133–134
black body 36
Black Hole of Calcutta 37
Blagden, C. 104
Bligh, J. 97, 160–161, 165, 174–175, 192
blood,
  –brain barrier 174
  chemistry 89, 93–95
  circulation 72–85
  flow 28, 153
body fluids 107–109
body size 25, 56–61
body temperature 14
  average 16
  metabolism 3–5
Boulder, Nevada 105
bradykinin 85

brain damage 152
broad-band control 160–161, 192–193
Brody, S. 59
brown fat 63–65, 133, 144, 146, 188
budgerigar 137–138
Burton, A. C. 8–9, 28
butterflies 112–113

cactus wren 87
Cahill, G. F. 64
calorimetry 44–50
 bomb 46
 closed-circuit 47–49
 direct 44–46
 gradient layer 45–46, 162
 heat sink 45
 indirect 46–50
 open-circuit 49–50
 respiration 46–50
 spirometric 48–49
Cambridge 174
camel 14, 192–195
Cannon, Walter 7
capillaries 77
carbohydrate 51–56
carbon dioxide,
 production 47–51
 wash-out 87–88, 93–95
Carboniferous 9
cardinal 91
caribou 76
cat 11–12, 98–99, 150, 154, 174
catabolic processes 52
catecholamines 64–65
cattle 88, 99–101, 150
central nervous system 85, 92–93,
 154
central receptors 151–153
central stimuli 162–173
chemical reaction 2
chemical thermoregulation 18–21,
 65, 151, 162–166
chimpanzee 98
cholinergic nerves 103
cicada 113
circadian rhythm 14–15, 116
circulation, skin 77–81
citric acid cycle 54–56
classical conditioning 139
climate 178–179
clo unit 30–31
clothing 28–32, 141
cockroach 111, 113, 116

cold, responses to 184–191
cold spots 148
cold tolerance 145
cold vasodilatation 76–78
comfort 142
compensation, physiological 5–6
conductance 72
conduction 23, 33–35
conductivity, thermal 24–25, 33–35
conformity, physiological 6, 110, 181
conservation of heat 72–75
control of body temperature 143–177
control systems 143, 157–162
convection 23, 35–36
cooling, rate of 24–25
core 15–16
counter-current heat exchange 72–75,
 80
cowbird 136
crabs 115–116
Crawford, Adair 44–45

Dale, Sir Henry 103
Dalton's law 37
Darwin, Charles 189
deer mouse 180
dehydration 108, 137, 195
deuterium 50
development 143–147
diffusion of water 96, 113, 120–121
dimensions, linear 25
disorders of thermoregulation 176–177
diurnal rhythm 14–15
dog 57–58, 75, 80, 88–91, 94, 98–99,
 149–150, 158, 174
donkey 101, 104
dormancy 129
dormouse 131
Douglas bag 49
drinking capcaity 108–109, 195
drugs 173–176
dry-coat 106

eccrine gland 96–102
echidna 11–13
ectothermic animals 4, 113, 143–144
Edholm, O. G. 8–9
Edney, E. B. 113
egret 89–90
eland 193
electrolyte balance 192–195
electromyographic technique 66-67
emissivity 36

endergonic (endothermic) reactions 52
endocrine gland 130
endothermic animals 5, 120
energy 69–70
energy conservation 144, 190
energy exchange 23
energy metabolism (see also metabolism),
body temperature 3–5, 18–21
heat loss 18–21
environment, thermal 1–2, 178–181
enzymes 2–3, 8, 69
epitrichial gland 97–102
ergometer 70
Eskimo 141
European Association for Animal Production 61
evaporation 23, 37–39, 86–109, 191–192
flight 137–138
respiratory tract 86–95
skin 96–109
excitation 163–173
exercise 70–71, 142
exergonic (exothermic) reactions 52–56

faeces 194–195
fat (see also brown fat) 28, 35, 51–54, 131, 187
feathers 28–29, 32, 80, 144, 146
feedback 158–160
Feldberg, W. 103, 174
fever 158, 176–177
fingers 76, 80
fish 117–120, 139
5-hydroxytryptamine (5-HT) 65, 174–176
food intake 138
forest 196–197
Fourier's law 25
fowl, domestic 28–29, 65, 80, 89, 135, 150, 152–154
fox 30
Frédéricq, Léon 81–82
frizzle fowl 62–63
frogs 121-122
fulminant hyperthermia 177

Galapagos islands 124–125
gas analysis 49–50
glaucous gull 186
glucose 52–56, 65, 69, 188
glycogen 62, 65, 94

goat 101, 104, 174–175
gooseflesh 184
gorilla 98
gradients,
physical 27
physiological 27
thermal 26–32, 72–75
guinea pig 146
gular flutter 89–92
Gulf of California 124
gustatory sweating 151

haemolymph 115
hair (see also fur) 197
hairless Mexican dog 63
Haldane, J. S. 49
hamster 131
Hardy, J. D. 36, 67
Harvard University 139
heat,
balance 19
conservation 72–75
energy 69–70
exchange 33–39, 72–75, 80, 86–87
flow laws 22–25
loss 20–22, 72–109
production 19, 40–47, 52–56, 61–76, 184–185
responses to 191–197
storage 22–23
stroke 104
Hellon, R. F. 155–156, 172–173
herring gull 75
heterothermy 5, 15–16, 74–77
Heusner, A. 115
Hoffman, R. A. 129
homoiostasis 7, 178
homoiothermy 3–21
core and shell 15–16
cost and value 7
diurnal rhythm 14–15
evolution 9–14
failures 17–18
hibernation 18
level of temperature 8–9
limitations 14–18
regulated temperature 16–17
hormones 19, 173–176, 184
horse 101–104, 106
human homoiothermy 162–173
humidity 37–39, 106–107
humming bird 133–134
hunting reaction 76, 188

208

husky dog   35
hyoid apparatus   89
hyperthermia   42–44, 106, 137, 177,
    195–196
hypothalamus   10, 14, 61–62, 85,
    92–93, 102, 122, 128, 138, 140,
    151–157, 174–177, 192
hypothermia   42–44, 65, 134, 145

ideal temperature   142
iguana,
    desert   92, 123, 127
    marine   124–125
inhibition   163–173
innervation of sweat glands   102–103
insectivores   131
insects   61, 111–116
insensible perspiration   96
Institute of Animal Physiology   174
insulation   13, 22–32, 72–75
    adaptation   185–191
    air   28–32
    coat   28–32
    external   27
    internal   27
    overall   32–33
    tissues   26–28
invertebrates   111–116
isometric contraction   70
isotonic contraction   70
isotopic water   50

Jenkinson, D. M.   97
Jurassic   9–10

kangaroo-rat   86–87, 192–195
kidney   108, 192–196
Kleiber, M.   59
Kornberg, H. L.   53
Krause end-bulbs   148
Krebs cycle   54–56
Krebs, H. A.   53

lactic acid   69
Laplace, Pierre   44–45
latent heat of vaporization   38–39
latitude   180–181
Lavoisier, Antoine   44–47
laws of thermodynamics   69–70
lizards   11, 41, 87, 92, 122–125, 128
load error   157–161
logarithmic charts   57–60
louse   112

Macquarie Island   136, 188
macro-climate   178–179
Malaya   106
mallee fowl   137
mammals (see also individual species),
    behavioural responses   135–138
    origins of homoiothermy   9–10
man   74, 76, 80–86, 88, 98, 110,
    140–142, 150–151, 162–173, 188–
    191, 196–197
marsupials   11–13, 87
Martin, Sir Charles   11–13, 111
mass   25
meso-climate   178
metabolic constants   51
metabolic pathways   53–56
metabolism   3, 40–71
    basal (BMR) 40–42, 139
    body size 56–61
    body temperature   3–5
    brown fat   63–65
    cold-induced   162–165
    cost   7–8
    development   143–146
    factors affecting   61–71
    maximal   185
    measurement   44–50
    rate of   3–5, 22–24
    reduction   196
    shivering   65–70
    standard (SMR)   40–42
    summit   184
    surface area   56–61
    thyroid   61–63
    voluntary activity   70–71
Meyer, H. H.   151
micro-climate   178–179
micro-electrode   155
micro-habitat   136
mitochondria   54, 62
moisture   32
molluscs   61
monkeys   98, 139, 174
monotremes   11–13
moths   113–115
moulting   181
mouse   59, 134, 139, 145
mouse-to-elephant curve   59
muscle   28, 65–71, 118
Myers, R. D.   174

NAD (see nicotinamide adenine dinuc-
    leotide)

National Institute for Medical Research 155
Naval Medical Research Institute 162
necrobiotic secretion 97, 99–102
negative feedback 158
nervous integration 157–173
Newton's law 24–25, 30, 33, 43
Newton, Sir Isaac 24
nicotinamide adenine dinucleotide 55
nightjar 130
non-shivering thermogenesis 64–67, 188
noradrenaline 64–65, 103, 174–176
Norway 117

on-off control 157–158
ontogeny 143–147
operant conditioning 138–140
oscilloscope 149
ostrich 94–95, 196
oxidative phosphorylation 55, 62
oxygen consumption 47–52, 61

pain 148–149, 151
panting 87–95
  efficiency 90–92
  origins 87–88
  regulation 92–93
  respiratory characteristics 88–90
  secondary effects 93–95
paradoxical cold 158
parasympathetic nervous system 103
parental behaviour 137, 145
partition of heat loss 33–39
Pavlov, Ivan 139
pelican 89
penguins 136
peripheral circulation 72–81
peripheral receptors 147–151
peripheral stimulation 162–173
periodic heterothermy 18
perspiration, insensible 31, 96
phosphocreatine 69
photoperiod 181
physical thermogenesis 65
physical thermoregulation 18, 65, 151, 169–171
pig 88, 99–101, 135, 139–140, 146
pigeon 89
pilocarpine 103
platypus 11–13
plethysmography, venous occlusion 79–80
Pliocene 196

poikilotherms 3–6, 111–128
polar bear 186–187
poorwill 91–92
positive feedback 158–159
Precht, J. 182–183
precocial development 144–146
proportional control 158
Prosser, C. L. 6, 183–184
protein 51–54
protozoans 60
pyrogens 176–177
python 126

Q_{10} (see temperature coefficient)

rabbit 83, 150, 155–157, 174–175
radiation 23, 36–37
rat 98, 139, 145–146, 154, 187
rate control 158
rate processes 182–184
reference temperature 17
regional heterothermy 15–16
Regnault, Henri 47–48
regulated temperature 8–9, 16–17
regulation, physiological 6, 181
Reiset, Jules 47–48
reptiles 87, 92, 96, 157
respiratory centres 92–93
respiratory quotient 50–52, 130
respiratory system, birds 94–95
roadrunner 136
rodents 87–88, 131–132
rotation (acclimation) 183–184
RQ (see respiratory quotient)
Rubner, Max 20, 56–58, 65–66
Ruffini corpuscles 148

salt 107–109, 192
saturation 37
sauna bath 104
Schmidt-Nielsen, K. 14, 192–195
Scholander, P. F. 44
scrotum 150–151
sculpins 120
seasons 180–181
second-phase breathing 90
set temperature 17, 157–161, 169–171, 177
sharks 117–118
sheep 88, 99–101, 146, 151, 154, 174–175
shell, 15–16, 25
Shiefferdecker, P. 96–100

210

shivering 19, 65–70
  development 144
  efficiency 67–68
  hormones 175
  insects 114
  nervous control 68, 163–165
shrew 187–188
size, body 25
skin 28
  circulation 77–85
  isotherms 163–164
  receptors 147–151
Skinner, B. F. 139
snakes 127
soaring flight 137
sparrows 136, 146, 196
spinal cord 154, 157, 165
spirometer 48–49
splanchnic circulation 85
squirrel 30, 131–133, 146, 196
steady state 8–9, 22
stoker's cramp 107
Stussi, T. 115
sun 36, 197
surface area law 56–61
sweating 84–85, 96–109
  anatomy of glands 97–99
  classification of glands 96–102
  efficiency 106–107
  evolution 102
  fatigue 104–106
  gustatory 151
  regulation 102–103, 169–171
  salt loss 107–109
  sensitivity 171
  water supply 197
sympathetic nervous system 83, 103, 133
synapses 175

technology 110, 141
temperature,
  adaptation of body 185
  biological activities 2
  body 14
  coefficient 2–3, 42
  compensation and adaptation 5–6
  critical 20–21, 43–44, 72, 126
  environmental 1
  ideal 141
  limits 2
  receptors 147–156, 172–173
  regulated 8–9, 16–17
  set 17, 157–161, 169–171, 177

skin 72–77, 162–173
  upper and lower critical 20–21, 126, 184–185
thermal circulation index 28–29
thermal conductivity 24–25, 33–35
thermal environment 1–2, 178–181
thermal gradients 26–32, 52, 72–75, 185
thermal homoiostasis (see homoio-thermy)
thermal insulation 13, 22–32
thermal sensations 147–150, 166–168, 171–172
thermal steady state 8–9, 22
thermodynamics, laws of 69–70
thermogenesis (see heat production)
thermoneutrality 20–21, 41–43
thermostat 158–159
three-forths power law 61
thyroid 61–63, 130, 188
  hormones, 61
  –stimulating hormone (TSH) 62
Tierro del Fuego, Indians of 34, 189
tissue conductance 26–27
tissue insulation 26–28
torpor 18, 129–135
total ventilation 88–90
touch spots 147
translation (acclimation) 183–184
tree creeper 136
Triassic 10
tricarboxylic acid cycle 54–56
trout 119–120
tunny 117–118
turtles 127
two-thirds power law 61
tympanic isotherms 163–165
tympanic thermometry 162

Uganda 124
unit recording 155
United States 141
urea 51
uric acid 51
urine 194–195

vagus nerves 92–93
van't Hoff effect 2–3
vapour pressure 33, 37–39, 72, 96
vasodilatation, cold 76–77
vasomotor activity 76–85, 184, 191–192
  human limbs 81–85, 108, 146

211

venous occulsion plethysmography 79–80
ventilation, respiratory   86–93
Voit, Karl von   58
voluntary activity   68, 70–71
voluntary dehydration   108

warm spots   147
water balance   108–109, 192–195

water intake   138, 141, 195
Weddell, G.   148
whales   35, 74
work   69–70, 142
wren   136

zone of thermoneutrality   20–21, 41–43